To Gen

From

THE
GARNETT
CHRONICLES

Also by Johnny Speight and published by Robson Books

THE THOUGHTS OF CHAIRMAN ALF

THE GARNETT CHRONICLES

As told to Johnny Speight

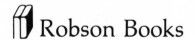 Robson Books

First published in Great Britain in 1986 by Robson Books Ltd,
Bolsover House,   5-6 Clipstone Street,   London W1P 7EB.

Copyright ©1986 Johnny Speight

British Library Cataloguing in Publication Data

Speight, Johnny
   The Garnett chronicles.
   I. Title
   828'.91407   PR6069.P4

ISBN 0-86051-402-1

Photoset by Grainger Photosetting Ltd., Southend.
Printed by Whitstable Litho Ltd., Whitstable.
Bound by Dorstel Press Ltd., Harlow, Essex.

Contents

Publisher's Acknowledgements

We feel we owe a special debt of thanks to Dennis Main Wilson for his research and hard work as Editor of *The Garnett Chronicles*, and to Janet Law who so ably assisted him.

We wish to thank all those people and organizations who have lent us photographs for inclusion in the book, as many of those from Mr Garnett's private collection quite often proved unsuitable for reproduction.

Thanks, therefore, to Denis Selinger (p. 60) *Radio Times* and BBC Enterprises (pp. 8, 18, 27, 32, 40, 52, 60, 64, 65, 72, 73 and 81), The Photo Source (pp. 46, 47, 52, 90, 93, 95, 104, 105, 108, 110 and 112), Johnny Speight and Helliar & Sons for the West Ham team photos (pp. 96 and 59) – and, again, to Dennis Main Wilson (p. 122).

Photos of Mr Garnett, his family and neighbours, show Alf played by Warren Mitchell, Mrs Garnett (Else) played by Dandy Nichols and their daughter Rita by Una Stubbs; their neighbours Min and Bert by Patricia Hayes and Alfie Bass, Mrs Hollingbery who lives upstairs by Carmel McSharry, Winston Spencer Churchill, whom Mr Garnett insists on patronizing by the name of 'Marigold' by Eamonn Walker and Arthur, Mr Garnett's drinking companion, by Arthur English. Since Mr Garnett and Mrs Garnett seemed to have had a tug of war over many of the photos we wished to use, we have been compelled to borrow some originally taken for the BBC television series 'Till Death Us Do Part', produced by Dennis Main Wilson, and 'In Sickness and in Health', produced by Roger Race.

Prologue

Mrs Hollingbery, that thing upstairs, said to me one night, I was sitting there, she was cooking me my supper and I was going on about something or other and Mrs Hollingbery turned to me and said: You ought to write it all down.

What? I said.

Where the world went wrong, she said. You've got a pencil, she said, an some paper. If you ain't, I have. I've got a pencil, she said, if I can find it.

Look on the mantelpiece, I said. There should be a pencil up there ... does it write? I said. Cos if it does I'll start tonight.

An I did.

I'm not a scholar – although, to be truthful, I know more than most down our street. What I mean is I don't know no Greek nor nuffing. That don't matter, said Mrs Hollingbery. The Greeks won't want to know where we went wrong.

So here it is – my first book. Not the first one I've read – the first one I've writ.

ALFRED GARNETT ESQ.

9

1

In the beginning ... in the beginning see, God just made the one person in HIS own image and likeness – Adam, so's HE could look at him and see what HE looked like. HE'd have done better if HE'd made hisself a bloody mirror. Cos Adam was God's first mistake.

Where God went wrong, see, if HE will forgive my saying, HE tried to be fair to Adam and gave him his own soul and freedom of thought; and of course, not having God's wisdom, Adam's first thought was – WOMAN. And that is where yer trouble started. Course, God, being a compassionate God, and Adam being HIS first creation, let HIS kindness rule HIS wisdom – took a rib, made him a woman and SEX reared its ugly head.

Course Adam – not being too bright in the head (well he hadn't been here long) – didn't realize in order to get what he wanted from a woman, he had to give her a say in things and listen to her soppy ideas about how the world should be run.

If God had known what woman was like before HE made her, HE'd have given her arms and legs and things just to perform man's will. But what HE wouldn't have done is give her a mouth.

So, if it hadn't have been for man, a man's need for a home help – someone to clean and wash up and look after his house for him – woman wouldn't have got born at all.

An except for a couple of special women like yer two Elizabeths – the First and Second – the world would have been a better place without em. I mean, let's face it, what can they do that adds to yer culture of yer world? They can't play football, they can't play cricket. They can't do nuffing except yap! yap! yap! yap! Drive you to drink they do. Like I asked Mrs Hollingbery to get me a pencil an she ain't sharpened it. See, with women you gotta do every little thing for yerself.

The wife passed on a few weeks ago, she was the same: heart in the right place but no mind to speak of. I said to her one night I said, fetch my carpet slippers, luv. I watched her go upstairs, could hear her hunting about in the bedroom . . . finally she comes down. She says, I can't find em. I say, they're here, my luv, down here by my chair.

Women! Gotta do all their thinking for em. Anyway, I buried her a few weeks ago, laid her down to rest, give her a good send off like – God rest her soul. Could've give her a better send off if it hadn't been for that bloody undertaker. Robbing swine! He wants to reduce his prices that's what he wants to do. He's a crook, that's what he is, taking advantage of the bereaved, fleecing poor people . . . Three hundred pounds for a coffin, three hundred pounds to carry it, forty pounds a bloody car. The cemetery's only round the corner, we could've walked there, carried her ourselves. I'll never use him again as long as I live. They talk about the cost of living, what about the cost of dying?

Could have been a lot dearer next year, Mrs Hollingbery said. That's not the point, I said, not the point! Why'd HE have to take her? There's all the villains in the world, murderers, rapists, football hooligans . . . why'd HE have to take *her*? What'd she done HE had to take her? Nuffing I'd done!

It was a nice funeral though, Mrs Johnson said, I think

she'd have been pleased. I think she'd have been pleased if she could have seen the way she went. Not the point, I said, not the point. It could've been a lot better, the money I paid him. She wouldn't have been unhappy, Mr Johnson said. Pleased she'd have been it went all right for her, Mrs Hollingbery said. Not the point, I said. It should've been better, that's my point. For what I paid that undertaker it should've been better, for what he charged me it wasn't much! I thought we'd have got more for the money he charged, that's my point! He wasn't cheap! *That's my point!*

You done well though, Arthur said. Done well? I said. On the money I mean, I mean, on the money you had, Arthur said. He could've done better though, I said, on the money he had. It wasn't cheap! It didn't look cheap, Mrs Johnson said. Very tasteful, Mr Johnson said. She'd have been pleased, Mrs Johnson said. She wouldn't have been unhappy, Mr Johnson said. He charged enough though, I said.

An then I'm over at the barrel pouring meself a drink an I hear Fred Johnson: Wasn't many turned up, he says to Arthur. No, Arthur says, it wasn't the best of turnouts. Bloody cheek! An then that old boot across the road she says: They ain't got many friends. An then her upstairs, Mrs Bloody Hollingbery, says, looking at me: There'd have been more turned up if it had been *him* we was burying.

Marvellous annit? There's a roomful of booze I've laid on for em ... I said, never mind about me Mrs. It'll be a happier day when you go! I dunno how I'm going to manage, do I? They've taken her half the pension away an the thirty pounds a week she got for sitting in that wheelchair. I mean, I'm over fifty pounds a week worse off! Fifty pounds down the drain with her going! There might be only one of me now, but it's no saving, I can tell yer! There might be only one of me, but it's still gonna cost me as much for me electricity. There might be only one of me but I've still got to burn the same light as when there was two of us, an I? Don't matter if there's ten people in here, fifty even, you still got to burn the same electric to light a room, the same heat to warm it up ... if half of em leave it don't get no cheaper. If all of em go an leave only me it still costs the same!

I watch the telly ... it still costs the same as when she was here watching it with me! It ain't got cheaper now she's gone, I still gotta pay the same licence money, I don't get it no cheaper now cos there's only one of me watching it now instead of two, oh no! Look, there's ten people down the road, Pakis, watching the same film on there I'm watching, but it don't cost them any more than it costs me because there's ten of them, do it? There's only one of me watching, but I don't get it no cheaper, do I? I still got to pay the same licence fee for my telly with only one watching it as they do with ten of em watching it ... An they talk about economics! Them up there in that bloody Parliament! They know no more about economics than ... I wouldn't trust em with a jam jar of threepenny bits.

You want to know about economics? I'll tell you about economics. When a rich person dies, the ones they leave behind are always better off. All right, they try an look unhappy, not too pleased like about the money they've been left but ... Praps they are unhappy, I mean, it's on the cards the person they lost was sort of close, or, you know, they sort of liked em praps ... but they're not out of pocket on it, are they? They're better off financially cos they inherit what's left. I can't inherit what Else has left. All she had she could leave me was her pension an what she got out of being in that wheelchair. Which she would have left me, willingly, I know ... but she couldn't, cos yer bloody government's grabbed it back, annit? It ain't fair!

14

See – when yer Queen dies (God forbid!) Charlie becomes King. Right? Because he inherits. But Philip don't have to draw his horns in, do he? He's not left worse off because of it, is he? He still sits down to his same breakfast, he still gets his same amount of dinner, his pipe ain't empty, he still knows where his next pint is coming from. If he wants to ride on the Royal Yacht he still can, it's still there. Look, a better similar: yer Queen Mum, she lost her husband, right? She didn't lose half her money, though, did she? Granted, she had to move out of Buck House, but they found her a house just as good. An she's still got her box at Ascot, an her cabin on the Royal Yacht – an she's not living on supplementary benefit at Clarence House with the DHSS telling her how many bars of electric she can burn in the winter . . . she shouldn't have to, she's a wonderful woman. But nor should I have to!

It was the government killed her off, my old lady. We all know that. We all know who it was. They froze her out. Hyperthermia. She froze to death. Go an use the telephone, they said, phone the DHSS. The bloody phone's vandalized, I couldn't even phone my Rita. Anyway, you'd need Scott of the Antarctic to find the phone under all that snow. Four feet of snow there was. Four feet? my Rita says. (Like her mother she is, don't believe a word I say.) You wasn't here, I said . . . It was too much snow for me, I said, I couldn't manage in it, I ain't got no bloody snow shoes.

But that was in February, Dad, Rita says, an Mum only died last week. She never thawed out, I told her, it takes well into the summer to get over an English winter.

That's true, Alf, Arthur says, there's parts of me still numb from last winter's cold. Coldest winter for over hundred years they said, he said. That's right, I said, an yer Army an yer Navy would've been issued with special warm clothing an rum rations, I said, but us, yer civilian population, is expected to sail into it unprotected!

We should be given special winter money for living here, I said. For staying in residence, an occupying the country during its worst months. Most of yer well-to-do are off into the sun well before Christmas. Leaderless most of the winter this country is, cos yer Parliament's never here for the winter. First blast of cold air an they're off. Off with the swallows, Arthur says. Right, I said. Don't wait for the swallows most of em. That's why you never get a war in the winter. It's true, annit? All our wars we've had have all been summer wars. Go through yer history, yer last war, yer First World War, yer Falklands . . . all started in the summer they was. An for why? Cos there's nobody here, nobody living in England, nobody of authority or importance, that is, who could arrange to start a war in the winter. None of yer Parliament, that is, none of yer political brass. Cos first touch of damp in the air, first chill wind an they're off into the sun.

That's why we've got yer coons over here – Marigold's mob. Pack em all off to England, yer politicians said, an we'll have this tropical paradise for ourselves, yer sunshine islands . . . too good for yer coons these are, too good for Marigold an his mob. Keep a few of em for servants, put white coats on em an stick a tray in their hand, but get rid of the rest of em . . . knock down their shanty towns an smarten the place up a bit. Build a few five-star hotels an use it for yer winter recess.

For the winter junkets more like, Arthur says. The politicians think, what a good idea, sitting in the sun out there, chinwagging about yer third world. Loosen yer belt to make room for another blow-out an let's see if we can't sort out this Ethiopian famine, he says. Send that back, send this back, not enough meat on the lobster, this steak is too rare, the champagne's too warm . . . oh yer, you won't catch none of them back here till the weather warms up, he said.

Course, Arthur's one of Kinnock's mob but there's sometimes something in what he says. Of course, yer politicians are out there sunning theirselves while we can sit here shivering an dying of the cold like my poor Else did. A good woman she was. A good wife an mother. An I'll never find better, I know that.

An then Mrs Hollingbery starts. It was them killed my mother, she says. They killed her off. That was hyperthermia. They froze her to death. (Crying in her gin she is by now.) A good woman my mother was, she says, a saint she was. A kinder woman never lived, she sobbed. (I'm sure she was, I thought, like you, I thought.) We had a plot for her, she sobs. Reserved special for her it was, an it was smart, an clean an decent when we first had it, when we buried my father in it. (The tears are flowing into her gin now.) You should see it now, she goes. We had to bury my mother in it a few months ago, you should see it now. You'd think it was pigs buried there. It's blackies now my sister said, it's them blackies, they're burying them here now . . . it's them what's made the mess. Well, if they are I said, says Mrs Hollingbery, if it's them they're burying here, if it is blackies – she's coming up. Mum's not being left to lie here among blackies I said. She couldn't bear em when she was alive, she's not gonna lie among em dead.

They've ruined our street! butts in the old boot from across the road. (If you ask my opinion it's her who's ruined the street if anyone has. Had the council round digging up the drains till they found it was her.) Well, they ain't gonna ruin my mother's grave, Mrs Hollingbery says, they ain't gonna ruin her eternal rest . . . they ain't laying alongside her them blackies ain't. I'll have her up. I'll have her up an lay her to rest somewhere else.

Mrs Hollingbery – that thing upstairs.

They shouldn't let em over here in the first place, I said, it's not their country. It's not their cemetery, says Mrs Hollingbery. If they must let em over here, at least send em back when they're dead. We shouldn't be made to have em here for all eternity.

Course, anything like that upsets my daughter right away. She won't have anything said about yer coons... an of course, Marigold, my black social worker home help, is at the funeral an he's listening to all this. Mrs Hollingbery, Marigold says, when you play 'God Save the Queen' or 'Land of Hope and Glory' on the piano you have to use the white keys *and* the dark keys...

Ooh... I didn't know you was here! Mrs Hollingbery says. Well, I know you can't see yer coons in the dark too well, cept when they smile... but we had the light on...

That's your excuse, my Rita shouts. You didn't know he was here. It's all right to abuse people but not so they can hear you, not to their face. That's English manners. Nobody's talking behind his back, I says, he knows what we think about him. I like him, but I'd like him better in his own country.

Look, I was born in this country, Marigold says. My father an my mother were born in this country for crissakes... What do I have to do to become an Englishman?

You can't be English, can you, Sambo, I says.

I am English! I'm black English! You're white English, Marigold screams at me. Wouldn't argue with you, I says.

Well, you can't. You can't argue with him, or my daughter. Waste of time it is, cos they only see the one side of any question – their own side. Trouble with all yer immigrants, you let em over here, show em the hand of friendship, show em a bit of equality... an the next thing they're demanding it. They was popular when they knew their place. Like yer workin class – they was popular when they knew their place. Every employer wanted em, an everywhere you went there was signs on every factory gate: HANDS WANTED. An that's what they wanted, not minds stuffed with Scargill an Karl Marx! I said to Marigold, I told him, I said, if you blacks was prepared to be a bit more respectful, a little bit more servile, you'd be popular again an every home would want one.

The funeral went all right though, or the wake I should say. A few of em had a bit too much to drink, but no harm done. Cos I mean, it was only out of respect to my Else we got drunk... you know, to give her a good send off. You got to do it right. I mean, people round this way, they set a bit of store on that sort of thing. I mean, the way you go, it's important ain't it. People save up for it, take out insurance to guard against it – not having a proper send off. I mean, I prefer a wake to a wedding myself. Seeing a man off on his way to Heaven is no occasion to be unhappy.

One of the best funerals down our road when I lived in Wapping was when old Mrs Fairclough at No. 13 went. Well, she couldn't grumble – she'd had a good run. Ninety-five. She had her share of the old age pension afore she went. I see her up the cemetery a few weeks afore she died, burying her oldest daughter Win. I had a little joke with her. I said, ere, I said, hardly worth your going home again, is it? She laughed! Well – many a true word. She had a good send off, though. Went off in a Rolls – course she'd have preferred the horses – she never liked cars. Well I mean, it was a grand sight in the old days, the horses four to a carriage, everyone lining the streets, and they never started the horses trotting till they was three streets away. Different now – they just rush you off now. Even go through red lights. Still Nugent's arranged it all very nicely – tea afterwards, everything. I always say when it comes to a funeral you got to go a long way to beat old Nugent. She laid in the house for a week before they screwed her down, and old Nugent made her look very nice. Best I ever seen her. Had her teeth in an all. Oak coffin, brass handles, bit of velvet. Well, I mean, he'd agreed it all with her beforehand, before she snuffed it. See, old Nugent he asked her, did she want to be burnt or buried? Cos it was cheaper burnt. Well, the land values has gone up. Well she said she'd rather be burnt, couldn't afford to be buried. But he was decent old Nugent, he let her lay in the oak coffin with the velvet and the brass handles till just before the off, then he transferred her to plywood. Well, the oak is a terrible price now and it's a shame to waste it. Same with the brass. I've heard they're even putting em down in cardboard now.

We had a whip-round in the street. People are very generous on these occasions. I was appointed treasurer – well, someone's got to do it. Hard work! But she was a nice old girl, though, wanted her to have the best, all that money could buy, so I thought I'm not going to penny-pinch so I ordered ten crates of light, nine crates of brown, two barrels of bitter, eight bottles of Scotch and six of gin.

Course, the funeral I enjoyed most was when they buried the wife's sister Maud. I couldn't stand her sister, I used to go to school with her. Bloody Maud, she'd show you her knickers for a bite of your toffee apple them days. Couldn't stand her. I mean, I get on with most people. But we had nothing in common. Tell a lie. One thing we had in common: I hated her and she hated me. But I hated her more than she hated me. I mean, her funeral . . . I don't think I ever sat through anything that gave me more pleasure. I don't know who was the happiest man there, me or her husband. I tell you: it was her husband. Must have been. But who enjoyed it most? Him. Must've done.

21

No. Nobody could have been happier than I was that day. You know what he done? Her old man Wally? He bought her the biggest tombstone I've ever seen. Must've weighed a ton. He said to me, Alf, he said, you know why I bought her that? Cos comes the day of reckoning, come the day of judgement, when we're all up there enjoying ourselves, I hope it's going to take her months, years, to move that. Buying time. That's what I'm doing, Alf. Buying time. Hoping, praying, I might get a few years, months even, weeks even, in eternity without her up there to spoil it for me. I tell you, Alf, he said, Heaven's all most of us has to pray for ... but if she gets to moving that heavy piece of stone, that expensive piece of granite I've weighed her down with an gets up there to Heaven ... it won't be Heaven no more. Leave it to her. She'll ruin it. Like she ruined our two-up, two-down outside toilet pissing all over the seat. I'm sure God's going to put up with that! HE might be a Christian, Alf, he said, but I'm telling you, if HE's got any kind of class at all, HE's not gonna put up with her, Maud. And I tell you something else, Alf. If HE is prepared to put up with her, I'm not. I'm sodding off down the other place.

Anyway, it went off very well on the day, except for our vicar. He stutters. I thought, he starts now she'll never get where she's going. Ain't half hard on the knees. I wouldn't mind if he only stuttered when we was sitting down, but he always seems to catch us kneeling. Apart from that it ain't fair, ain't fair on his parishioners. I mean, you don't expect God to listen to him do you, stuttering out his requests. Busy man, yer God. Big place Heaven, annit. I mean ... it's a lot for one God, annit. I mean, there's our vicar on his knees, stuttering for a new church, and I mean God's in a hurry, dashing off somewhere perhaps. Come on, come on, spit it out for Christ's sake – ain't got all day. Bloody fool ... Don't know why HE employs some of 'em.

Ain't heard from HIM for years, have we? God, I mean, never comes down here now though, do HE, on earth, not even for a holiday. Abbey ready, I'm coming down for holiday. I mean, HE could come down here sort out all our problems – South Africa, Russia, Brixton – and be back up there in time for tea. Wonder why HE don't. Not bothered praps. Praps HE don't know – you'd think people would pass it on, though. I mean, there's thousands going up there every day. You'd think someone would tell HIM. Tell HIM the state we're in. Still as I say, HE's a busy man.

2

I wish God would come down an have a look at things, have a look at some of the people we have to live with. I bet, if HE saw em, and some of their goings on, an what they're up to, HE'd wish HE hadn't made most of em. *I* wish HE hadn't!

Like when Else was alive an I was pushing her in her wheelchair – which she didn't make any easier, kept putting the brake on she did – I said to her, I said, leave that brake alone. I'll take that brake off, I'll remove that brake I will. Well, go steady, she said, take it easier. Take it easier! I said. You ain't making it any easier putting that bloody brake on. Look, if you don't like the way I push this thing...

Just take it easier, she said. I don't want you conking out on me, you're not as young as you used to be, you know. I know that, my dear, I said, I know that, an I'm getting older by the minute pushing you about in this bloody thing! You'll have to lose some weight, that's what you'll have to do, I said, sitting there stuffing yer face with chocolates. Oh, you'll soon get used to it, she said, once you get the knack. It only requires a bit of effort. I'm beginning to think it's a punishment from above, I said. It's me. It's *me* HE's got HIS knife into. HE's worked out what is the hardest punishment, pushing this bloody thing or sitting in it!

As I said to the woman up the DHSS, I said to her, I said . . . Look, I said, this bloody consultant my missus is seeing might be a very distinguished specialist, but we've only got his word for that. I mean, I don't know if he is, or he ain't, no more than you do, Mrs. We have to take his word for it. Only his mates, an the people who work with him know how good or bad he is, an they won't blab. All I can say from what I've seen of him, I'm not over the moon about him.

He's a clever man, Mr Garnett, she said. Oh yes, I said, well they all *claim* to be clever men, Mrs, an if they was as clever as they claim to be we'd all live for ever, but we don't. All I know is, when my wife first went to see him she couldn't walk, an now, after pushing her up an down to that hospital an back, an wearing three pairs of boots out seeing him, she still can't walk. An very soon, Mrs, the way things are going, I won't be able to walk . . . I'll be sitting in a wheelchair with her. Now, I'm not a clever consultant, Mrs, but I couldn't have done no worse than that.

Nobody's claiming the consultant can work miracles, Mr Garnett, she says. I'm not here for miracles, I tell her. No one can do much for her legs now, they're a write-off, I accept that. No one's going to get them going again, I know that, they're too far gone. But if you wanna help her, if you wanna give her a bit of quality of life, look after *my* legs. Cos it's my legs she's got to rely on now. It's my legs she needs, cos my legs are more use to her now than her own legs are. Save my legs. That's what you got to do, save my legs you wanna help her. Provide her with a powered chair, an electric powered chair, something I don't have to push, something that'll save my legs . . .

But Mrs Garnett is not incapacitated enough to qualify for a powered chair, she says. All haughty like. Like all yer bleeding bureaucrats! Oh, she's not incapacitated enough, I said, because she's got me, her loving husband, her live-in relative, bloody muggins, to push her!

Look, when I retired, Mrs, I tells her, when I retired, aged sixty-five – after a lifetime of slog an paying in thousands of pounds to you lot – I didn't bargain to be given another job harder even than the one I retired from, the one I was too old to work at, to be turned into a bloody horse, tethered to a bloody wheelchair for the rest of my life! I'm being treated like an unpaid social worker I am, Mrs. How would she be if she didn't have me, eh? But because I live with her, because she's mine an I love her, I got to push her! Well, it ain't bloody fair, that's all I got to say, it ain't bloody right.

If I was to leave her in the lurch, if I was to divorce her an live in sin with her, she'd get a powered chair. Well, I say it ain't right. All right, I said, I'll divorce her, I'll live in sin with her, an I'll write to the Archbishop of Canterbury, I'll tell him. I'll tell him I've been forced to live in sin with my own wife by the DH bloody SS just to get a powered wheelchair out of em! SS is right. SS! Sieg bloody heil the lot of em!

Well, it makes yer mad, dunnit? Bloody people! You pay into it all yer life! Another thing ... shows you the sort of rubbish God lets on this planet ... I'm pushing her home from the DHSS. There's cars parked all over the bloody pavements so I have to go in the road. An this bloody car driver honks his horn, leans out of his window an shouts out: Why don't you get on the pavement? Cos I can't get on the pavement, cos all you cars are on the pavement, I said. Pull over, he shouts. Look mate, I've got as much right on this road as you have, I said. Hurry up, he says. There's no law says how fast I've got to go, I says, all the law says is how fast I can't go. I had him there. You're not a road user, he says. I am using it, I said, I am using the road. I'm just in front

It's a funny thing. I hold my hat like that and people keep putting
money in it. I don't ask em. Well, it keeps the pipe filled.

of your car using it, I said. That got him. You're not supposed to be using it, he says, you're not a car, I'm a car. I'm a four-wheeled vehicle, too, I said. I pay tax to use these roads, he says, I've got a disc on my windscreen. An how do you know I ain't got a tax on *my* windscreen? I says. What windscreen? he says, you're a pedestrian. Not necessarily, I says, I might be a car driver who's walking. Anyway I've got a cripple in this chair I'm pushing, I told him. I'm sorry about that, he said. So you ought to be, I said. Look, be reasonable, he says. You be reasonable, I says. Pedestrians are not allowed to walk in the road holding up traffic, he says, you should know that. An who says I can't walk in the road? I says. It's dangerous, he says. It's a bloody sight more dangerous trying to walk on the pavement with all them cars parked on it, I says.

By this time I've reached a zebra crossing, an I thinks to myself, right, this is where I have him. Cos I know my rights on a zebra crossing like everybody else. So, I pushes Else in her wheelchair on to the zebra crossing an waits for him. Now what? he says. Go on, knock us down, I says. Knock us down on this crossing an I've got you. I'll take you to the cleaners, I said. I'll sue you for all you've got. I'm a pedestrian now, I says, a law-abiding pedestrian an I'm crossing the road in the right place on my legal right of way. Just hurry up, he says. I've got an invalid in this chair, I said, an she don't like to be hurried. Cross the road, he says, shouting, his eyes bulging. Cross the road! Cross it! Hurry up an bloody cross for Pete's sake! There's no law says how fast I got to cross it, I says. Anyway, I'm not sure which side she wants to go, you've confused her with your shouting and hollering.

Anyway, I starts to push the wheelchair across the crossing, an I gets almost to the pavement, an he's getting ready to start his car across, when I turns the chair round an starts to come back – I'm thinking I'll have a game with him – course, he's furious. She's changed her mind, I tell him, raising my hat. Well, this is the last straw to him, you see, an he's out of his car an grabs hold of the wheelchair. Take your hands off that, I said. Take your hands off that chair. I'll put my hands on you in a minute, he says, all bravado. Oh, will you? I says, will you? We'll see about that, I says. Cos I've done a bit. I could've won golden gloves if I'd stuck at it. An what this geezer don't know is who he's messing with. So he's in for a bit of a shock in a minute I reckon . . . an then I sees the silly moo has started to wheel herself off down the road so I has to run off after her, which is lucky for this bloke otherwise he was in for something he ain't bargained for . . .

That's what I mean about people, see, an how hard it is to get on with em. Like Fred Johnson my neighbour. We all decided to have a street party for Prince Andrew an Fergie. Well, I've got a table outside in the street an I'm putting the decorations up – you know, Union Jack, bunting, an all that – I'm up a ladder when Johnson comes out an says: Hoi! Move this table. D'you hear me? he shouts. I'm talking to you. Move this table.

Well, the table's up against his car an he can't move it an I suppose that's what's upset him. Sod off, I tells him, we're having a street party. But we don't wanna street party here, he says. You might not, I says, but I do. A vote was taken, he says, an the majority voted against a street party, he says, you know that. But the minority didn't, I tells him, the minority didn't vote against it. You want democracy, the minority's got to be heard. The minority was heard an was overruled, he says. But it didn't wanna be overruled did it? I said. This is a free country, mate, an the minority wanted a street party. But the majority didn't wanna street party, he keeps on. The majority ain't having a street party, I says, it's the minority's having a street party. Will you move this

29

bloody table, he says. Look, I says, trying to reason with him, all the people in my house voted for a street party an they're gonna have a street party. I wanna get my car out, he says, an if you don't move that table I'll drive right through it. You leave that table alone, I says.

Well one thing led to another an later on I let his tyres down, so I got me own back. Well, you got to, ain't yer? You can't let em push you around...

3

Is your Michael working yet? Else asked. No, but he's
had the promise of a job, Rita said . . . I had to laugh. Oh, I
said, he's still getting promises of work is he? He was
always getting promises of work when he lived down
here. There's a lot of unemployment in Liverpool, Dad,
my Rita said. I know, I said, that's why he went back
there, wasn't it? You're not funny, Dad, Rita said. I'm
not trying to be bloody funny, I said, you're the one
making the jokes. Promise of a job! He don't wanna
work. He never did, work is foreign to his nature. He
was unemployed when there was full employment. One
of the leaders of the unemployed he was. One of those
who helped make it popular he was. He couldn't wait to
get back to Liverpool an the security of mass
unemployment. The bloody proletarian paradise up
there, annit?

Look, if they're supposed to be so poor up there with
all their unemployment, how is it they can afford two of
yer most expensive football teams? If they're so poor
how can they afford all them star players? It's obvious,
annit? Yer welfare! Yer welfare's paying. See, some
draw their welfare an spend it with yer bookmakers . . .
but a lot more of it goes through the turnstiles at
football. Up in Liverpool they have European matches,
cup ties, league matches – they're playing three times a

31

My daughter Rita. You can see the likeness, can't you.

week up there, both teams. Liverpool an yer Everton. So where's the money coming from? Both grounds are always packed, packed to the rafters they are, an none of em's working. The whole town's on the bloody dole, so where are they getting the money from? Yer welfare! Bloody Everton an Liverpool are being subsidised by the DHSS. Both of em. Must be. An what ain't spent on football an in yer betting shops is spent in yer pubs! That's why we got banned out of Europe over them! Just cos of the ignorance of a handful of Liverpool louts, West Ham's chance of glory in Europe's been lost. It's not bloody fair. Years West Ham's been preparing for Europe – wasted years now ain't they? An just because of a few Liverpool louts getting drunk. Won't pay their rates, though, not like the rest of us will they? Oh no. Bloody troublemakers – we ought to brand em, with branding irons across the forehead, brand em for life, brand em so that we can see em, see who they are. 'Football hooligans' across their foreheads, 'muggers', 'rapists', brand em all an when we see em we can whack em . . . belt em . . . castrate em . . . string em up . . . Bloody swines!

Ignore him, the silly moo said. Ignore him. Oh yes, I said, ignore me. Is Michael's mum any better? she said. No worse, Rita says, they've found out what it is. She's got senile dementia. I'm not surprised, I said. Irish, ain't she? What's being Irish got to do with it? Rita says. Senile dementia is a failing of the brain, I said, that's what being Irish has got to do with it. Anything to do with the weakening of the brain an your Irish is prone to it.

Prone to it? she says. Of course they are, I says. Look, yer Irish ain't got much a brain to start with in the first place, have they? Yer Irish ain't noted for their brains, are they? Yer Irish are more noted for their ignorance than their brains, ain't they? I mean, it stands to reason,

We'd have won more down at West Ham but we play too fair, that's our trouble. An we're too honest. We don't put a bottle out for yer ref, I spose that's half of it. See, you're supposed to put a bottle of Scotch in his room every home game. They all do it – it's an old custom. Some might says it's bribery, but it's not bribery – it's sort of referee's perks. I mean, you're entitled to a bit of advantage on yer own ground. That's why, when a ref books a player he has to write his name down there an then, at the time of the incident, when he sees what he's supposed to have seen. An if his hand is clear an steady – well, it holds up. But if his hand is squiggly, an all over the page – well, they turn a blind eye to his complaint, cos he ain't supposed to touch the Scotch, see, till after the game. It's true. That's why it's so hard to win at Anfield, cos old Bill Shankly – he's a Jock – used to get his Scotch wholesale ... they probably give him more than the quota. Well, the game's changing an we've got to go along with it, I suppose, an start playing it the way the others play it. Have to ignore the subtleties and finesse of the game an get more like Liverpool. Mind you, not much point now we're banned out of Europe. All right, let em play the European Cup amongst themselves, won't be a European Cup without us will it? Be a Wogs Cup. Banning us out of Europe! They didn't want us banned out of Europe when Hitler was about did they? It was all, Hello Tommy, then. It was Tommy this an Tommy that. Have a drink, Tommy, ooh la la! Voulez-vous avec voire, Tommy. Come and liberate us, Tommy. Now it's, Piss off, Tommy. We should've left em to Hitler. He'd have give em football! He'd have give em bloody hooligans! I'll tell you something else – if old Gorbachev starts, if the bloody Russians start on em, it will be, Come back, Tommy, all is forgiven, Tommy! All right! String em up! String em up if you like. I don't hold with hooligans but we can handle our own hooligans – they're our hooligans an we don't need a load of bloody foreigners telling us what to do with em!

dunnit? If your brain is weak to start with, if your brain is a small, delicate, puny little thing ailing from the minute you're born, with hardly a glimmer of life in it . . . I mean, the least little bit of normal, natural wear an tear an it's gonna be liable to pack up, annit? It's the same with all yer Celts. Yer see, yer Celt is an old primitive strain, an he's not as highly evolved as what we are, is he? Endangered species he is, an he? Might even have become extinct by now if it wasn't for us, the English, protecting em, allowing them rights an things.

See, the trouble with yer Celts, yer Scotland and yer Ireland and yer Wales, is they wanna be like us and have a country of their own with its own Parliament, but they ain't big enough. I mean, all Wales and Scotland are really is parts of rural England – somewhere to go for yer holidays, that's all. What they should be is counties like yer Devon and Cornwall. I mean, let 'em have their own Lord Mayor, yer.

Same with yer Ireland. Shouldn't be the Irish Free State, should be yer County of – yer County *Borough* of . . . Oh! no they says, don't want that, we want Home Rule and our own language. What they want is a bloody good thumping like we give em in the old days – not a war, can't have a war with them. I mean, all those wars we had with em in the old days, they wasn't wars, they was more like blood sports. I mean, they even had the bloody cheek to say they had their own Queen in them days, didn't they, the Scots did – Mary Queen of Scots – bloody cow – she wasn't a proper Queen. Tried to get above her station, and what happened? She got the chop, didn't she. Well, they knew how to handle them in those days. Yer jocks are all right anyway. Don't cause much bother, cept at football. They're not bad at that actually – some of them. Bit dirty, but then all their brains is in their feet.

Mate of mine, old Ron, he's a Taff. Been here a few

years now, mind. They moved him to Wapping. Slum clearance out of South Wales. Proper ignorant he was when he first come here. Thick as two boards. Couldn't speak English hardly at all. We used to have a laugh at him. He said everyone in his village spoke this sort of Welsh language. Language! I told him. I said, listen Taff, it's not a language, it's a kind of dialect. No, he says, we got words and everything, he says – we got words for drink and words for eating. I told him, I said, listen, I said, yer natives have that, they have sounds for things, but it's not a language. I mean, a dog barks, but it's not a language. I mean, yer Jocks and yer Irish, they've got that. They got sounds like yer Gaelic, but it's no good to them except for talking amongst themselves. They want to talk to other people, they got to learn English, see. Trouble is, it's beyond their grasp for most of them.

I mean, yer Welsh – we even had to teach em how to dig coal. The trouble with yer average Taffy, see, he's nothing much more than a two-legged pit pony really. In fact, yer pit pony could pull more coal and was cheaper to run. Blimey! I'll tell you what, if yer mine owners had of had their way, yer Welsh would have been extinct by now. Blimey, they was getting rid of them faster than yer Julius Caesar and his Romans did. Course, you can always tell yer Welsh – they speak like Pakistanis. Also they got all these little holes in their faces. Could come from trying to eat with a knife and fork, but it's more likely that it is the coal pox. They used to carry all the dust home in their faces, see. And the mines was losing thousands until they installed the pit-head showers and made them wash before they went home. You know, it's a pity there ain't no coal mines out in Ireland, cos they're good with shovels Micks are, born to it ain't they. I mean, give a Mick a shovel and a big hole and he'll keep digging until he comes up the other end.

4

The *real* rot started with Jack the Ripper, otherwise known as Gladstone the Jew, the scourge of the flower of British womanhood, specially in Wapping, where he lurked in the foggy streets. Everyone in Wapping knew that Gladstone was Jack the Ripper, an as people said, course he's the Prime Minister, cos if you're going to be a sex pervert an attack girls and women in Wapping, what better way to remain undetected than by becoming Prime Minister? The last man people would suspect. Cos if you happen to be the Prime Minister and you meet a copper just after leaving the scene of your foul crime, he ain't going to say: What're you doing here with that black bag? is he? He's going to say: Hello sir, Mr Prime Minister, Mr Gladstone sir, how are you? An that's how he got away with his foul perverted crimes.

So, with a mass murderer as Prime Minister and the Royal Family growing weaker, England had to struggle on, and with the customers of Marks and Engels growing greater in number, a black cloud loomed over the coast of Merrie England, this once glorious land of Henry the Eighth and West Ham United. This Royal Throne of Kings, this precious stone, stuck in a silver fortress built by nature herself for slinging yer arrows at outrageous fortune. Course he was a local lad – Billy Waggle Dagger, as he was known in his native Wapping which is where he lived. Well, he was working over at

Southwark in his Globe Theatre. Wouldn't live there though – lowest of the low that side of the river. Course when he made a few quid he moved to Stratford Broadway – in the East End. Not Stratford-on-Avon, or as it was known in them days – Stratford New Town. Well, they had this slum clearance round here even in them days.

I had a letter from the Labour Council saying they was going to demolish *my* house – slum clearance – *me*! I mean, her next door – *that's* a bleedin' slum! I wrote to the Prime Minister. I warned him. I said: If your Labour lot demolish my house, they touch one brick out of my home, I'm warning you, I shall leave the country. I put it in the letter. I said: Adolf Hitler couldn't knock my house down, but you're going to, you bolshy bastard. Never even had the decency to reply an I put in a stamped addressed envelope – probably nicked the stamp. Well, they'll nick anything – bloody Labour.

Old Bert and Min next door – they moved them out, put em in a bloody great tower block. Bert wasn't too pleased. Well, it's his chickens. Unsettled em all that way up there, can't get a decent scratch – it's all parquet flooring, can't seem to get their claws going. And Min wouldn't use the lift – frightened of it she is. I mean, they're on the thirty-fifth floor. Bert says they're looking down on the aeroplanes. He says, they moved in on the Monday an he didn't see his Min till the Friday. He says, Where the bloody hell have you been? She said, I've been scrubbing the steps. Bloody fool – hearthstoning em she was. And you ought to see that bloody flat of theirs. I mean, the walls are like paper. Old Bert told me he opened the oven door one day, there was a fella from next door dipping is bread in their gravy.

I told old Bert – rent strike, mate, rent strike. Pay rent for that bloody dump! They sent a bloke round from the Town Hall with a rent demand, little blue form, shoved

Min and Bert. She always fancied me more than her husband. I seem to have that thing with women – never took advantage of it though, cos I was always true to Else. A lot of em thought I looked like Clark Gable.

it under the door. I was there. I told old Bert, I said, Get yer bellows out. I blew it back again. So the fellow shoved it under the door again. I blew it back again. Kept it up for half an hour. Finally the bloke got fed up. He knocks on the front door, Bert opens it. The bloke said, Ere, are you the geezer what won't pay the rent? Bert says, Yes. Well I don't blame yer, says the bloke, I wouldn't pay rent for a draughty bloody flat like that neither.

As I say – the Stratford where Shakespeare lived was here. *Facts* – he was a local lad. He spent his summers in Southend which is where he wrote *The Tempest* on the pier. He used to sit there for hours with his fishing rod and his notebook, looking up the Channel, his feet dangling in the water. That's also where he wrote 'There'll always be an England'. And like Othello, the Moor – Othello, the coon. I don't go and see Shakespeare much these days. We done it all at school. Well, they don't do him proper. I saw yer Lord Sir Laurence Oliver in *Othello* – on the telly it was. He blacked up like, and did a bit of Sonny Boy – but I mean, he ain't no Al Jolson is he? But in that play, Shakespeare knew that if you let yer coon marry a white woman it don't work. Cos a white woman can drive yer coon mad, see. Shakespeare knew that. I mean, that handkerchief bit: yer coon comes home from work and finds his wife – the thing that married him – he finds her with a handkerchief that belongs to his friend and of course there's blue bloody murder. He wants to start killing everyone – cos your coon he's unstable like that. Well, I mean, if I come home and found the missus using handkerchief what belonged to old Bert next door, I wouldn't go in and row with him. Blimey – it probably got mixed up in the laundry or blew off their line into our yard. Anyway old Bert don't use a handkerchief – I wish he did. Uses his cuff he does – dirty perisher.

And take Hamlet. The lessons of permissiveness. Course that lad went mad. Wouldn't you? I mean, come home from yer holidays in Denmark and find yer uncle's poisoned yer father and is now having it – well, you know – with yer mother. I mean, imagine young Prince Charles coming home on leave from the Navy and finding his dad, Philip's had a dose of arsenic in the earhole – and his mum – well I mean, she wouldn't do that sort of thing. She's above it. But it just shows you what your permissiveness can lead to – and that was yer point Shakespeare was making.

Course, in yer old days of yer Globe – when Shakespeare run it himself – it was more like a Palace of Varieties then. As you went in they give you rotten fruit to throw at the actors. Sort of audience participation – and which they enjoyed. And that is why Shakespeare give em long speeches – them soliloquies to do – so's you could sort of get yer eye in with yer fruit. You know, have a few practice shots. Now of course you see it, an them long speeches is boring cos you miss the throwing bit.

I went up the Old Vic to see one of his plays – the missus couldn't make head nor tail of it. I got fed up explaining in the end. Nothing like a Palace of Varieties. A bloke told me to put my pipe out. I mean, blimey, you got to sit there all that time without a smoke. And you can't get a drink. I mean, in the old days they brought drinks round where you was sitting – big chesty ladies. You need a drink in yer theatre, I mean, some of the rubbish they bung on ... You need more than a drink. They expect yer to sit there for bloody hours, can't talk, can't smoke, can't have a drink – complain and they say you're putting him off. What I say, if he was doing his job proper he shouldn't be able to hear us talking among ourselves. I mean, you never hear footballers complaining about people drinking an talking among themselves ...

The trouble with yer theatre, it's too much like a church. If they let you have a drink in church an sit there with a fag in yer mouth, people might go a bit more. People would go to a lot more places if they could have a smoke an a drink. People would ride on trains more if they could smoke. Bloody home help we had before I got Marigold . . . I'd just lit me pipe an she starts. You're not going to smoke that thing in here, she says, are you? What's it got to do with you, I says, I'll smoke it where I like won't I, it's my house – bloody cheek! Well, I'll not stay in the same room with that thing, she says, waving her arms about knocking my smoke away. It's a filthy, dirty habit, she says. Get off, I tells her, pipe tobacco's all right, pipe tobacco's healthy enough. It's dangerous, she says. Dangerous? I said.

Makes you laugh, dunnit? You smoke one of these, I tells her, an you'll come to no harm. But she won't have it. It's dangerous to be in the same room with somebody filling it with that poisonous stuff, she says. Geroff, dangerous, I says. Even if it was dangerous it wouldn't stop me smoking, Mrs, cos I'm smoking for the health an prosperity of the country, I tells her. For what? she says. Where does yer nation derive its biggest income from? I asks her. Answer me that, I says. Yer tobacco tax, I tells her. See, if the whole country stopped smoking, all that money's down the drain annit? Almost come under yer sabotage act that would, ruining yer country's economy. No, I tells her, see, what I'm doing is patriotic, cos it's patriotic to smoke, annit? Rubbish! she says, cos she's an ignorant cow. Not rubbish, I says, *not* rubbish. Do you know the amount of money collected on tobacco tax every year is enough to pay for yer entire National Health Service? An a bit over? I pointed to the wife. She wouldn't have her wheelchair if it wasn't for people like me smoking, I tells her. I mean, blimey, I says, us smokers ought to get a medal for what we're doing for the country, an people like you, Mrs, who are too frightened to smoke because of health reasons, you ought to be given the white feather. If a war breaks out, if we was to declare war on someone an you're called to the colours, I mean, you can't refuse to go out an fight because it's dangerous, can you? Well, it's the same with yer smoking, annit? You don't give that up because it's dangerous, do yer? Not if it's for the benefit of your country. No, I'm smoking for England and the Queen – God bless her.

An another thing, I says to her, your doctors wouldn't be so against it if they was able to earn out of it. If yer smoking was treated like a National Health drug like all yer other drugs an yer doctors could prescribe it, they'd be all for it, wouldn't they? It wouldn't be harmful then, not if yer doctors was getting bunged for prescribing it like they get bunged for prescribing all the other drugs, oh no. Go in to see him with a cough then an he wouldn't be saying give up smoking, oh no. He'd be writing out a prescription for Havana cigars or something, saying, these might do your cough more good, try a couple of boxes of these. An I could say, if I'm his patient like, tell yer what I'd like to try, doctor, I'd like to try some of them big ones old Churchill used to smoke. An he'd say, all right then, I'll put you down for a couple of boxes of them, see how you get on with em. Course he'd be getting bunged wouldn't he? But because your doctors ain't getting bunged I'm persecuted, smoking me pipe in me own home, Mrs, in me own country I'm persecuted for smoking a pipe. What is it – Russia? In me own country, country I fought for, I'm persecuted, treated worse'n a black, I can't smoke on a train, I can't smoke in a tube train, I can't even smoke on the platform. I can't even smoke in the street in peace even without somebody poking their nose in, casting aspersions on some bloody poster, waving their bloody arms about shouting filthy habit!

I'm on a train – bloody British Railways, bloody paid for out of our taxes, an bloody fares what's a crime – sitting in the smoker where smoking's allowed, where yer sposed to smoke, an a crowd of bloody Asians get in, Eastern nig-nogs, bloody Pakis – not even in their own bloody country they ain't, stinking of bloody curry they are – an cos I light me pipe, an Englishman in his own country he was born in (where *they* won't wear a crash helmet cos they wanna wear a turban), sitting in me own bloody train, an they start waving their hands an bloody arms about like a pack of dervishes cos I'm smoking, an opening the bloody windows they did. I'm sure Winston Churchill would've stood for that! I'm sure any bloody foreigner told him to put his cigar out in his own country, or anyone else's bloody country for that matter, would've got his answer: Open the window!

All right I'll open the window, she says. Oh no you won't, I said, not in my house you won't. You won't come in my house, bullying an attacking old people. In my house you'll do what I say, I told her. This is where I live, Mrs. This is me! This is mine! This part of the Empire is still mine, Mrs. This bit here is still free, here I do as I want. Here I smoke in peace an no bloody arm waving or windows open. An she starts banging her great fat chest. These are my lungs, she says, an I don't want em bunged up with your filthy smoke! I can see em, I said, all four tons of em. I wanna breathe pure, she says. Well, pure off an breathe somewhere else, I says. I fought a war, I said, against people like you, Mrs.

Bloody home helps! I hate em. I mean, they're given a good job looking after people like us, but they don't show a bit of gratitude. I tell yer, they're not worth the money the council pays em. My house is like a tip, disgusting it is, dust everywhere, sink full of dirty crockery. It's getting so scruffy I feel ashamed to invite people in.

This is what teetotalism leads to. Didn't smoke, didn't eat
meat, liked newts – the Ken Livingstone of his day. Whereas
Churchill – there's a man liked a drink, an he smoked, an he
ate meat, an he was a better leader for it. I'd like to see Ken
Livingstone tell him to put his cigar out on the tube.

Course, they say it's my fault cos I'm scruffy. But it's their fault. I mean, they're the ones getting paid to clean it up.

Of course the missus – God rest her – used to be up at the crack of dawn tidying the place up, scrubbing an cleaning, getting it ready for when the home help arrives. An of course, when they arrive ... What would you like me to do, Mrs Garnett? they say. I tell em, what we would have like you to have done, I tell em, we've done it already. Cos you was late, you was supposed to be here at nine o'clock. I left home at nine o'clock, one of em said to me, my day starts when I leave home. Does it? I said. Well, as far as I'm concerned, Mrs, your day starts when you get here. Anyway, don't let's have no arguments, I tells her, we'd like more work than arguments – cos most of em will stand there all day leaning on a broom talking if you let em. So, come on, I says to her, chop chop. You can make a start on the bedroom. I've already tidied in there, the missus says. Never mind, I says, she can tidy again, an besides there's some shirts an underpants in there I want washed. I'd like to point out to you, Mr Garnett, this home help says, I'm not supposed to do any work or clean any rooms used by active relatives. Solely used, I points out to her, I've got your book here, Mrs, I says, so don't come the old soldier with me. I don't use that bedroom solely. She shares my bed with me. Poor woman, she says. Never mind about poor woman, I says. I'll tidy *her* half of the room, she says. You'll do both halves of the room, I tell her. You can clear your own mess, an wash your own underpants, she tells me. I'll do anything Mrs Garnett wants, she goes on, but I'll not be your dogsbody. You'll do your job, that's what you'll do, I tells her, I got your book here, Mrs, so don't try any strokes on me, I know my rights. An I know my rights, she says.

I reads her book to her: The type of work which your

home help can be expected to do is those tasks which you cannot perform due to handicap, illness or infirmity. You're not handicapped, she says. No, I says, but my wife *is*, an her tasks which she cannot perform is looking after me, annit? Cleaning up in *my* house, cooking, washing, scrubbing an performing all the duties a wife performs for her husband. That's your job, I tells her. An that's what the council sent you round here to do, to work. Not to sit about drinking cups of tea. An to start with I ain't had no breakfast, I tells her. Haven't you had no breakfast, Mrs Garnett? she asks the missus, ignoring me. No we ain't, I told her. Cos the silly moo's been too busy trying to get the house clean an tidy for you, she ain't had no time yet to cook me any. I told her to leave everything for you, I told her, you don't have a dog an bark yourself.

Do you want me to get you some breakfast, Mrs Garnett? she says, still ignoring me. Course we want our breakfast, I tells her. I told you we want breakfast! We've been sitting here waiting for it for the last two hours for you to turn up. Don't think you're getting away with that two hours, I tell her, cos I've made a note of it. I'll get that docked out of your wages. You won't get away with no skiving here, Mrs, I'll put you straight on that now. We're not simple in the head like some you look after, I told her. Also, I says, for your information we know what we've got an what we ain't got. What do you mean by that? she says, all innocent like. We've had home helps before, I says, an we've had things go walkies. Well, she's up on her high horse over this. Says I'm insulting her, says I'm insinuating she's a thief. I said, never mind what I'm insinuating, I'm your employer an I can insinuate what I like. You just consider yourself lucky you got a job, I tells her, consider yourself lucky there's people like her – pointing to the missus – people lame an infirm providing work for you. You're lucky, you're in a new industry, I tells her, yer Welfare and Health Service, the new growth industry. The patients get nothing out of it, but your lot, you're doing well out of it. The more diseases an illness there is, the more the doctors can't cure, the more customers you get. The worse off we are the better off you are. What I'm always telling Marigold but he can't seem to grasp it: a sick nation means more prosperous doctors an social workers. A criminal nation means more prosperous lawyers an judges.

Of course, Marigold's a pufta, but fair dues, I must admit, he's the best home help we've had. It was funny the day I come home an found him ... I was having a drink with Arthur in the pub, you see, an he was going on about something he's seen on yer telly – he loves his telly, old Arthur does, he believes everything he sees on there ... it's true, he says, it's true, he says, I seen it on the telly – well, this day he's on about how they put woman's hormones into yer bull's ear. I seen it, he says, I seen it on the telly. What woman's hormones, I said. Stuff em in his ear they do, says Arthur, you know, with a syringe, an it makes yer bull fatter. What, hormones does? Yes, hormones, he says, woman's hormones, they blow him up like, so you can get more meat off him. What hormones? I says, woman's hormones? Yes, he says, woman's hormones. An here's the danger, he says, if you get a bit of his ear, or a bit what's been close to his ear. What, his head? I says. It can turn you into a pufta, he says. But you don't eat yer bull's head, I said. You do eat yer bull's head, he says. No, not his head, I says. Yes his head, Arthur says, you do eat his head. You eat his head in yer mince. Geroff, I says. It's true, he says, I seen it on yer telly. No, I says. In yer hamburgers, he says, you eat it in yer hamburgers. No, I says. You do, he says, what you're eating in yer mincemeat an yer hamburgers is yer bull's head ... an it can turn you into a pufta. What,

50

yer woman's hormones? I says. Yer woman's hormones, he says. That's why we've got so many bloody puftas springing up like mushrooms all round us, spreading yer Aids an yer herpes.

I don't believe it, I says. It's true, he says, I seen it on yer telly. They should put a warning notice on it, a government warning, this hamburger could turn you into a pufta. Not if you're a woman, I says laughing like. Well, you got to have a laugh, an yer? It could have a reverse effect, Arthur says. What d'you mean a reverse effect? I says. What – woman puftas? Lesbians you mean? Why have we got so many? he asks. Same thing, ain't they? They're the same as yer man pufta only different – you know what I mean – where they enjoy it, where they do it, is unnatural. I mean, consenting adults is all right up to a point. Long as you ain't got too many of em, I says, seeing his point, but I've heard, Arthur, I tells him, I've heard yer Parliament's full of em. I mean, a few nancy boys, you can have a laugh at a few of em, but a line's got to be drawn. Cos we don't want to end up with a brown hatter in No. 10 Downing Street, do we? eh? With his live-in boyfriend. It's the mince, Arthur says, it's yer mince an yer hamburgers in yer Commons Dining Rooms. Yer woman's hormones, I said.

Well, I mean, we had a good old drink up, me an Arthur, an I thought no more about all this woman's hormones business an yer mince an all that – cos I don't often have mince – an I gets home, an lo an behold, who's in my house? Me new home help Marigold, a black pufta, an what's he got for me lunch? Mince! Bloody mince.

I went straight back up the pub. It's at times like that you need a drink. Alternative medicine, my dear, as I said to the missus. Alternative medicine. The Queen swears by it. Alternative medicine, she says, sneering like. Whisky – cos she never likes to see me drink, I dunno why – is that what the Queen swears by? No, but her

51

Marigold, my home help. Real name Winston Spencer
Churchill – disgraceful!

mother does, I said, an she's fit enough. She's older than you are, my dear, I tells her, an she don't have to be pushed about in a wheelchair, and she's still got all her marbles. That upset her, cos she don't like me inferring that she's not all there at times. But she ain't. She's going senile.

Look, I said to her, this stuff does yer far more bloody good than half the pills the bloody quack would stuff down yer throat if yer let him. Remedy, this stuff is, annit? Old remedy. Old Scottish remedy. Brewed up in your Highlands as remedy for raw mornings an even colder nights. Why d'you think yer Jocks put it in their porridge? If you've got nothing on you but a kilt you need something warming going down there. Kill any germ this stuff will. An it'll kill you too, she says, if you don't ease up on it. Oh yer, I says, I wouldn't mind a quid for all the colds an influenzas drinking this stuff has prevented me getting. You've always got colds, she says. There's a lot of colds about ain't there, my dear, I says. Can't avoid em all, can yer? I mean, there's times when I ain't drinking this stuff, ain't there? What times? she says. Look, I said, it's when you're asleep in the middle of the night that yer germs strike you, annit? Four in the morning, my dear, ask any doctor, that's when you're at yer lowest ebb I tells her, that's when yer germs strike, when any protection this stuff might've given you has worn off, when your defences are down. I've had colds. All right, I said. I admit it. But think of all the colds I might've got if I hadn't had this to fend em off with.

You really believe in that stuff, don't you? she said. Well, I says, I ain't found much else worth believing in. I won't say nothing about religion, I tells her, but yer Lord drank, didn't he? Eh? I mean, you may not need to drink up there in Heaven, but while yer Lord was down here on earth he soon discovered he needed a drink. As holy as he was, he soon found out he couldn't live down here

53

among us mortals an go through what we have to go through without having a few – drove him to drink we did. I bet his mum said, I wish you wouldn't go down there, mixing with those people cos you always come back drunk. Oh yer, he saw the need for it all right. Well, I'm not against it. Well, I mean, drink . . . it helps you to live with people don't it? I mean it helped me to live with her, you know, Mummy. Before she went. I mean, I'm not saying nothing against her – good woman, as women go. I mean, I could have done better. I mean, most of us could. What I mean is, if you was starting again, you'd sort of know more, like, what you liked, what you want from a woman.

I mean, it's like eating, annit? You go in a café, order what you think you fancy, and sitting next to you, your mate, see, he's got something better on his plate, something more to your liking. See, if you'd had a few drinks, if you're a bit drunk, it all tastes all right, dunnit? I mean, it's the same with your sex, annit? A few beers, have a skinful, and cor! Anything will do. But you can live to regret it.

I met my missus when I was drunk. Come out of the Green Man, well pissed, and we see these two girls, and Old Bert says, Cor! Fancy them, eh? So I said, yeah! So we started to throw stones at em. Well, I mean, you got to break the ice, ain't yer?

As I say, I courted her drunk, I married her drunk, and I was drunk when I, you know. Well, you got to give em a kid. Give em something to do, dunnit? Bring it up. Don't want em sitting about doing nuffing. As I say, it was drink brought us together. But you can't drink all the time, see. And it was the bits in between that was the trouble.

Well – it's an aphrodisiac, annit. A few beers and Cor! Give her one, right? An what's funny, see, it also acts like a contraceptive, cos well, sometimes you can't, can you? You know, like yer brewer's droop, see. You know, what the kids say with this maryjuanna – you know this: what yer wogs grow – they say if you smoke it, it makes the old sex bit last a bit longer? I mean, waste of time, annit? I mean, have a skinful. Quick fumble and kip.

Trouble is, though, with yer woman, they don't stop making demands, unnatural demands. Like when we was first married, there was hardly a month went by without her wanting, you know. And if I didn't, I got me food slopped up.

I mean, let's face it, sex ain't a thing the working class is used to. Not that kind of sex – pleasure sex. Ain't got time for it. I mean, you can't expect a working man to come home after a long day's work and entertain his wife with sex when he might want to watch telly, or go up the pub. It's aping yer aristocracy. Cos they have it with their concubines – which is different to your wife, and better than your television. But unlike your Caesar and your old Popes and your Peers of the Realm – the working man can't afford such pleasures, can't afford your girls for fun. All right if they issued them on the Welfare State – sex on wheels – but of course, your women wouldn't stand for that. It'd be, no, you're not having one of them in this house.

It's all this women's lib that's the trouble. I mean, in the old days, when a woman married a man, bloody grateful she was not to be left on the shelf. It's the bloody telly I blame it on. Before that come in the house, she didn't know nothing and the moo she was ignorant, and better off for it. That's what's unsettled her. Sitting in front of that all day, letting them stuff her head full of nonsense. Half this house is mine, she said. Oh! is it, I says. Well let me tell you about your half of this house. It's stuck to my half, and that's where it's bloody well staying. I wouldn't mind, but she's no good with the housekeeping. I give her nearly half of what I earn, but

Arthur – he likes a drink.

she's always on the earhole for more. Never mind about women's lib, I say, what about *man's lib*? A man gets married, he employs a wife but he ain't given the same conditions of labour what your employer of industry gets. I mean, you take your employer. Your ordinary employer. Right. He employs someone, and if that someone ain't up to the job, I mean if they're a bit lazy, like many of them are in industry today, he can sack them, see. But a husband, see, when he employs a wife, and she ain't turned out like he thought she would, he's stuck with her.

Like the other night, I'm asleep, see, and playing for West Ham. We're playing Barcelona in the European Cup Final. Ground's packed out. I've scored eight goals before half time. John Lyall's screaming out, Go on Alf, play it your way – it's your ball – go on! I'd just made a monkey out of Lineker. I got the ball, showed it to him, but took it away from him. Here y're – it's on me right foot. No it ain't, it's on me left foot. Now yer see it, now yer don't. It's on the back of me heel, no it's not – it's on me 'ead. Come on Lineker, keep up! Bobby Moore come up to me afterwards. I've seem em all, he said. Pele, Eusebio, Maradona, but you, Alf, you're something else. Comes half time we're thirteen up. There's Terry Venables – he's going mad. He's on his knees to John Lyall. How much do you want? I'll give you anything you ask. Robson steps in. He's mine, he says, he's mine. I'll build a team round him. All the girls are yelling: Alfie, Alfie, we want Alfie. They're all there – Raquel Welch, Myrna Loy, Joan Collins, and then bang! – silly moo wakes me up with a cup of tea. I bloody slung it at her.

Look at Arthur now, my mate, he's having trouble now with his missus. She's playing him up, not pulling her weight. But he can't sack her. He can't even dock her for time off. I mean, she's always round her cousin's, never hardly home. She ain't earning round there is she?

What I mean is, he shouldn't have to pay her for sitting round there. I mean, she couldn't do that if she worked for someone else. But there you are, say anything these days an they're off. They wanna divorce. Well, that's not fair is it? I mean, just for argument, supposing my silly old moo, God rest her, had asked me for a divorce. Well, that could've cost me, couldn't it? Could've cost me a lot of money. I mean, some soppy bloody judge might've give her half my house, an say I'd got to keep her for the rest of her life, an her sitting about not doing a hand's turn for me. I mean, you get the sack from any other firm, they don't keep you. They don't give you half of the factory an tell the guvnor he's got to keep you for the rest of your life. Let her have the dole, yer.

I mean, you take yer big football clubs – that's a better similar, see. I mean, they got a player who's gone off, an he ain't doing his proper job for the club, like scoring goals an whatever. You don't sack him you put him up for transfer, right? Because a football club wants to get back some of what they've paid out, don't they? I mean, it's only fair. I mean, old Arthur, me mate, he ain't satisfied with his wife no more – just for argument's sake, right? (Well, he ain't anyway.) So he puts her up for transfer right? I come along, and I'm in the market for a new one, so I go over the pros and the cons with him, look at her form, give her a medical check, and say right, now, I've got this wife I wanna dispose of first, before I can enter into negotiations with you. Let him look her over, see if he's interested, and if he is, well, we might be able to do a swap. With just, perhaps, a bit of cash changing hands. I mean, my wife might have a better wardrobe than what his wife's got – well she has, judging by what Arthur's wears. Or it might be some other thing that he reckons is worth a few quid extra. Nothing that meets the eye – like his wife is a good cook. Now if it was Mummy I was trading in I mean, we'd have

My team and the three lads who won the World Cup for us in 1966. Bobby Moore: Captain of England and West Ham. The only time that lad got his name taken was when the Queen asked for it to pin a medal on his chest. Geoff Hurst: he gave the Germans 'secret weapon' in that final – cor, dear! And Martin Peters.

to come to some arrangement on that, because I'd have the advantage there. Cos Mummy's cooking ... Well, what I mean is you couldn't very well place any value on it. I mean, that'd be something you'd have to play down a bit.

A woman who is not owned by a man, is invariable unhappy, sort of fretful. So you see, when you pick one out, the one that takes yer eye, be firm from the beginning. Kind! No need to beat them or anything. Train em right and you will find that they are friendly little creatures and easy to live with.

Else took this at Southend. Well, you got to go in the water, haven't you? One of the watering holes of yer Empire-builders. After sweltering in the unholy places of the Empire, like India and the Black Hole of Calcutta – all those hot places, brushing the flies off you – it was a relief to get home an cool off at some place like Southend or Margate. It's part of our English Channel. Trouble is, the French has the use of it on the other side which causes much of your pollution. You got to be careful you don't tread in something French that's floated over. It was a good day out, though. Have a few soon as you get on the coach. Don't have to be stingy with it either, cos you stop at the Halfway House on the way – you got to stop to load up again. An it's straight on to Southend and the Ivy House till closing time. Then cockles and whelks, a paddle an a bit of a kip till they open again. Ah! a bit of fresh air does you good. One year old Bert – cor he had a skinful! He was sick, fell under a bus, cut all his head open, wet himself, lost his false teeth down the toilet. He enjoys a drink, old Bert does.

5

Mrs Hollingbery's getting hard to live with. She was all right while Else was alive, always popping down she was then. Can I borrow this, can I borrow that? an not always quick to return what she had off us. But now Else has passed on, Mrs Hollingbery is always going on about having to live in the same house alone with me, an having to share the same front door with me. I don't know what she thinks I'm gonna do. She says she's worried about what people might say about her living in the same house as an unattached male. I says to her, I says, look, you got your half the house, I got my half, an I ain't coming up no stairs after you. An of course she's always moaning at me not to forget to bolt the front door when I come in at night. Silly cow! I dunno who she thinks is gonna come in after her. Old pickle face! Bring a sex maniac to his senses she would.

I mean, the other night. I'd been out. I'd had a few drinks – I admit that. I'd been up the pub an then back to Arthur's for another few. Well, you need a bit of company, cos it's rotten on yer own. But I was quiet coming in, an I didn't forget to bolt the door. I bolted it this night all right. I popped my head into Rita's room to say goodnight, let her know I was in sort of thing, an went to bed. Well, I'm sound asleep, when about three o'clock in the morning I'm woken up by Mrs Hollingbery. She's in my bedroom in a panic shaking me an shouting out: Wake up, Mr Garnett, wake up! Wake up! Shaking an pushing at me she is. Wake up! Come on, wake up! There's someone at the door.

Who is it? I said. I don't know, she said. Well, open the door an see, I said – I dunno, you gotta do all their thinking for em. I'm not opening it, she says, I don't know who it is. Could be anyone, she says, you open it. What time is it? I says. I'm awake now, an I can see it's still dark out. It's gone two, she says. You don't think it's burglars, do you? Burglars? I says. What, knocking for us to let em in? I says.

By this time I'm at the front door, her traipsing behind, an I'm just about to open it, when a thought strikes me: muggers! Could be muggers. Hooligans. Cos we're surrounded by em where I live. I mean, our street is home for em. I step back from the door – I'm not a nervous man, but you got to be careful this day an age – an I says to her, phone the police. Off she goes, an then she comes back. We haven't got a phone, she says. Useless women are, in a crisis. An all she's doing is standing there moaning, what we gonna do? What we gonna do? I dunno, I says. Open the door, she says, it might not be anyone. Of course, it's someone, I says, who d'you think's knocking? No, it might be all right, she says, praps something's happened, perhaps the houses is on fire an they're knocking to tell us – an she looks around sniffing. Look, I said, if the house was on fire I'd think we'd be one of the first to notice it. Can you smell anything? I says. Only you, she says. Well, I ignore that. I'd been drinking an women are all the same, they can't bear to smell drink on a man. Anyway, all this is going on, an whoever it is outside is still banging on the door. Who is it? I shout. Who are you? It's me. It's me, Dad. An of course I realize who it is, it's my Rita, an I've bolted her out. An then I hear, B'wana, open up! Bloody Marigold! She's been out all night with Marigold.

The Queen, God bless her. Put the Great back in Britain – give her the same powers the first Elizabeth had. A bloody big sword and a meat block.

Waiting for the so-called home help to turn up. One o'clock an I
ain't had my breakfast yet. Not fair, is it?

I open the door, an let em in, an instead of being sorry an apologizing to me an Mrs Hollingbery for knocking us up an getting us out of bed at that time in the morning, they just look at us an start to giggle. An Rita says, Oh . . . I'm sorry . . . we didn't know. An then I cotton on. There's Mrs Hollingbery in her nightgown an me in me underpants an they think . . . An Marigold says, You old stag. An then Rita says to Mrs Hollingbery, I didn't realize . . . I don't mind, she says to her; But you might've told us, she says to me. Well, I'm speechless an Mrs Hollingbery is furious. Well! she says, I hope you don't think . . . An they both burst out giggling again cos they do. And Mrs Hollingbery, outraged, or making out to be, runs upstairs an slams her door.

How long has this been going on? Rita asks me. How long has what being going on? I says. And all the pantomime making out he didn't like her, says Rita. He had me fooled, says Marigold. But I'm past caring now what she thinks about me an Mrs Hollingbery; what I'm more interested to know is what she's been up to out all night with Marigold.

You know what time it is? I says to her, coming in here with him, showing me up with the neighbours, you wouldn't be doing this if your mother was alive. Doing what? she says all innocent. You know what, I says, I don't have to say it, do I? An . . . with *him*! With *him*! God you make me sick you do, she says. I make you sick? I says, *you* make *me* sick! I'm going to bed, she says. An what's he doing? I says, pointing at Marigold, who is standing there with a big grin on his face as if it's all very funny to him. What's he doing? I ask her again. Ask him yourself, he's standing there, she says. He's not sleeping here, I says. God! Rita says, if it wasn't so ludicrous! Winston's not interested in girls. It's not girls that turn him on. I only wish it was . . .

Well, that's a nice thing for a daughter to say, annit?

That's what it means to be a parent these days, to have yer children go against you an turn away from all you believe in, and have tried to bring them up to believe in. Winston is who I call Marigold. A gay. A gay? He's a bloody brown hatter! An black!

What d'you mean, you wish it was? I says. What d'you mean, you wish it was girls he liked? Because he's so handsome, it's a waste, Rita says. But he's black, I says. So what? she says.

Like I told you, she won't have a word said against em, she won't. Blacks or bloody queers! Like I was saying to Arthur the other day, cos he's not too hard on em either, he tries to be liberal about em. I said to him, I said, look, Arthur, when yer government gave em permission to come out of the closet they didn't know there was so many of em in the bloody closet! We got em everywhere these days. They always sat with their backs to the telly one time. Sitting facing it reading the news they are now. Yer, well, it'sa more open society now, Alf, Arthur says. I mean, in the old days, there was more prejudice in them days. Yes, I says, an we was better off for it, wasn't we? Well, it's a free country, Alf, Arthur says. It was a free country then, Arthur, I says, it's always been a free country. We've been known for it all round the world for being a free country, but we still didn't allow things to go on that go on today though! Did we? We was a free country but we didn't allow the permissiveness they allow today! You can be a free country, I told him, without letting people go around doing exactly what they want to do.

How? he says. No, come on, Alf, he says, you can't have it both ways – you can't be a free country if you don't allow people the freedom to do what they wanna do. Control, I says. Control. Discipline. Control? he says. Discipline? What, in a free country? (Cos he's all right, old Arthur, but he don't understand the

67

subtleties.) You can't have a free country without controls, I tell him. For instance, I says, I'd like to be free to come into this pub an drink without the like of them in here. They bought you a drink, Arthur says. Marigold an his boyfriend had bought us a drink, see. Not the point, I said, is it? Self-discipline, that's what I'm talking about. Something they've never heard of, but something we've always known about. Not allowing your base an unnatural feelings to rule you like they've done. If God had wanted them to be queers an behave like women, HE'd have made them women an give em women's things in the first place. HE wouldn't have made em in the shape of men an given em men's things. They're a mistake, people like that.

An now I've got my daughter saying all the same things to me. Yes, she says, he's black an he's gay an I like him, and what's more I can go out with who I fancy. It's a free country! It gets on my wick all this free country I keep on hearing about, I don't mind telling you. Look, my dear, I says, it might be a free country out there, but in here, in this house, it's my home! You said it was my home, she says. Come back here an live with me, you said, she says, cos this is your home, your real home. It is, I says, but it's my home too. If it's my home, she says, I can bring who I like into it. An if it's my home too, I says, I can ask em to leave. If I came back here an lived with you, she says, that's where my home would be, out there in the kitchen, tied to the bloody cooking stove an the washing machine, same as it is for any woman who's fool enough to live with a man! Oh gawd! I thought, here we go, bloody women's lib again.

For your information, my dear, I said, when you marry a man, an I don't mean the scouse layabout you married, a real man I'm talking about. One like you? says Rita. Marigold starts to giggle but I soon shut him up. Not one like you, that's for sure, I said. Facts that women's lib close their eyes to, my dear, I says, is who is it has to go out into the real world, the hard world outside of the cosy comfort of her home an slave for yer woman, eh? An who is it slaves for him like an unpaid lackey in the cosy comfort of his home? she says. An who is it goes out an slaves to pay the rent for his home so it can be cosy an comfortable? I says. *His home?* she screams. An hers, I says, an hers if she wants to live with him. He's working his fingers to the bone trying to keep a roof over her head, but no, yer women's lib don't take no account of that, that's what's expected of him! An who is it who's expected to fetch an carry for him? she says. An who is it keeps her fed an clothed? I says. What's he supposed to do? Do his own cooking when he comes home from work? Keep a dog an bark heself.

Dog! Dog! she yells at me. That's what you want, annit? A dog to cook an clean for you! A domestic animal who'll wag its tail when its lord an master gives it a pat on the head or tosses it a bone when he gets back from the pub after spending most of his money with his cronies! A dog'd be more grateful, I tells her. A dog knows where its bread's buttered. Little did I know when I was creating you I was creating a rod for my own back, I told her. You want children, you struggle for em, an you go on struggling for em against all the adversities to bring em up wanted an loved. You dote on em an provide for em. I worked, as God is my maker, I worked hard! I never had much but what I had was brought into this house an spent on you an your mother. I cried some nights. Cried an prayed I could do more for you. I worked all hours, every bit of overtime that was going I worked it ... I come home here some nights my back breaking ... I couldn't lay on me bed with the agony of me aching muscles I'd strained working for them I loved ... crying an praying to the Good Lord to give me the strength to carry on, not knowing that little baby, that tiny infant in its cot would be poisoned an turn into a serpent at my throat, poisoned an corrupted by bloody women's lib!

An you needn't stand there laughing, I shouts at Marigold, you black fool, cos you're no better! You let em stuff your head with their rubbish too. You've got nothing to laugh about. You've killed the goose that laid your golden eggs too. What golden eggs? he says. Us! Us! I says, The British Empire! Your benefactor what looked after you when you was under us in the old days of yer Colonies. Trouble is you wasn't smart! If you'd had a bit more upstairs in them curly nuts you'd have known when you was well off. You wouldn't have got so uppity. You'd have let well alone. You were popular in them days when you knew your place in God's scheme of things an served those placed above you, before you let the socialists fill yer heads with all their rubbish about equality an all that crap!

By now, her upstairs is down again, complaining about us keeping her up. She can't sleep with all the noise, she says. I can't sleep, I tell her. An what's he doing here? she says, looking hard at Marigold. He's sleeping on the sofa, Rita says. Why? says Mrs Hollingbery. Cos it's softer than the floor, I spose, says Rita. What's it got to do with you anyway? I ask Mrs Hollingbery. This is my house, this bit here, where you've barged into without bothering to knock or anything, an in a few hours' time it'll be his day for cleaning if you must know. I like to keep the place looking tidy, if you don't mind.

You're not entitled to him now, Mrs Hollingbery says, not free help, not now Mrs Garnett has passed over to the other side. An then to Marigold, she says, Did they tell you about my door? Who? Marigold says. You work for the council, don't you? Mrs Hollingbery says. I'm just home help, that's all, says Marigold. Well, help me with my home then, she says, help with my door. You can tell em I want my own front door. With my own bolts an a chain. Cos I don't want no more of what went on tonight. Nothing went on tonight, I says. They woke me up with their knocking, she says. Yes, I says, they woke me up with their knocking as well. But nothing they think went on.

Have you been in touch with the council? Marigold asks her. I haven't spoke to em, Mrs Hollingbery says, I tried to phone them from the callbox round the corner. An she tells me there's a message writ for me in that callbox. Yes, I says, I know, an if I find out who wrote it ... Not that one, she says, this one is pinned on the wall: 'Tell Mr Garnett Rita phoned.' Well, why didn't you tell me? I said. I've told you, she said. *Before*, I said, you should've told me before. I'm not a messenger boy, she says. It's all right, I'm here now, says Rita, there's no need to fight about it. That was last week.

When you see your council, Mrs Hollingbery says to Marigold, tell em it's me, I'm the one who wants the door. Tell em where I live. You expect me to pay your milk bill for yer, I told her, but you won't even give me a phone message. Who did you speak to when you phoned? Marigold asks her. One hundred, the operator, she says. No, Marigold says, when you got through to the council, who did you speak to? An twice last week I had to get up an let your cat in, I told her. She wouldn't put me through to the council, Mrs Hollingbery said. She said I had to put money in the box first. Well, of course you got to put money in first, I says. (She don't know how to use the phone. They put em there, all instructions. She can't read.) I'm an old age pensioner, she says, I've got no money to waste putting it in phone boxes. I told her, it's private, I said, it's council business. It's their house. The police is free, the fire brigade is free, the ambulance is free, why can't the council be free? It wouldn't hurt em, they charge enough for it.

71

Eastbourne. Dead and alive hole. Not like Southend.

Maud's funeral. Best day of my life. We might have run out of glasses, but we didn't run out of booze.

You tell em what I said, she says to Marigold. Pass the message, I want a door put on my stairs. Tell em it's Mrs Hollingbery. They know where I am, they know where I live, they know where to come when they want the rent. I won't vote for em again, tell em, if I don't get my door. It's the last vote they're getting out of me, tell em. I wouldn't have voted for em last time, she says, if it hadn't been for *him* – pointing at me – persuading me. I've never voted Labour before. If my husband was alive he'd turn in his grave, she said. I didn't know how to tell the priest, she says, they burn down churches they do, the Reds. Oh yes, the Reds are worse'n the blacks, says Marigold.

You voted Labour, Dad? asks Rita. Look, I did it for yer mother, I told her, not for me. Labour's better for yer handicapped, that's all. I wouldn't do it again. Unless they put your pension up, says Rita. Are they? I says, then I caught her smiling. Well, I don't care if they do, I said. I don't vote for self-interest. Anyway, I says to Mrs Hollingbery, we got a front door! Yes, she said, but I have to share it with you, an while that might be all right for you, it's not all right for me. I don't want people talking about me. I don't want my good name blackened. I don't want people pointing me out in the street, saying, there she is, that's the one, living in the same house, sharing the same front door with a man, an unattached male. I'm not silly, you know. I know em an their slanderous tongues. You're one of em, I said. I know the sort of jiggery pokery they'll think we're up to in here alone, especially after tonight's goings on, she says. I don't care to have my name linked with yours in that way, thank you, or in any other way if it comes to that. Look, Mrs, I says to her, you ain't got to worry about me! The last thing I wanna do . . . anyway, it was you in my bedroom. D'you hear me? I shouted up the stairs after her. It was you in my bedroom!

She's mad, I said to Rita an Marigold. She's mad. Not for you, she ain't, says Marigold. She's about as fond of you, he says, as I am of Enoch Powell. Yer, yer, I said. That's what she'd like to make out. That's what she'd have you believe. They're all the same women! Hark at the bus pass Casanova, my Rita says. Yes? I said. Well, give her half a chance an she'd have me walking down the aisle, I can tell yer.

What're you talking about? Marigold says, she can't stand you. You're not very bright, Marigold, are you? I says. I grant you, that's the impression she tries to give, but if you had anything inside that curly nut of yours, Marigold, you'd realize that women always make out they don't want what they can't have. An you reckon she wants you? Rita says. It wouldn't surprise me, I said. An she's just making out she don't? says Marigold. You're getting near it, I says. An that's why she wants those stairs boarded up an her own front door, Rita says, with bolts and chains on it to protect herself from you in case you ever feel like creeping up there... An giving her one, says Marigold.

Shurrup you, I tells him. Uncouth little swine! An you say, Rita goes on, it's all just a come on, an she'd go to all that trouble, making out she don't want you, only because she knows she can't have you? Yer, I says, fantasy, annit? Fantasy. You women – you build fantasies, you love em. It's that romantic trash you read, all them soap operas you watch. Women read em, they do, an sit dreaming some Arab prince'll come along an carry em off on the back of his horse.

It sounds to me more like you're the one with the fantasies, Marigold says. Like you fantasize England's gonna beat the West Indians at cricket... not this century, man. Shurrup, I told him. Look, I said, what she wants is to build that door with its bolts an chains an have me break it down an carry her off kicking an screaming, an subject her to my will. It's what they all want, what they've always wanted, women! Look, I said, it's nearly bloody daylight an I've not had any sleep at all tonight what with you an her . . . I'm going to bed . . .

Well, next night, I'm going out, you see. I'm going up the Legion with Arthur – well it's a bit of a change. Makes a change from the pub. You know, have a few beers somewhere else . . . An I'm just putting me hat an coat on when down the stairs comes Mrs Poison Ivy. You going out? she says. Why d'you think I've got me hat an coat on for? I says. Well, she says, just see that you're in by half past ten. What? I says – I can't believe what I'm hearing. I'm bolting that door at half past ten, she says, an if you're not in, you can stay out. Look, I said, I please myself what time I come in. Please yourself, she says, but I'm still bolting that door at half past ten. I'm not going through last night again, she says, I didn't get a wink of sleep with all the commotion . . . I'm taking a sleeping pill at half past ten, she says, after I've bolted that door. An if you're not in it'll do you no good knocking. An tell your daughter. She's not here, I said, she's gone back to Liverpool. It's a pity you don't go with her, she says. Look, I says to her, you just leave that door, I'll bolt it when I come home. If you're not home by half past ten, she says, don't bother, cos you won't get in.

Well, the silly old moo never done that to me, threaten to bolt me out. I mean, bloody cheek. Look, I tells her, I'm master in my own house! Yes, she says, an you'll be master outside it if you're not back in it by half past ten.

Well, I mean, I've never had this before. I can't let her win. I mustn't let her get the upper hand. But at the same time, I mean, she has got an advantage on me. I mean, if she was to bolt it . . . She wouldn't dare! I gave her a good look. You know, a good stare. Eyeball to eyeball, like. Let her see what she was up against, sort of thing . . . An I said, eleven. She just stared me right out, the cow! Look,

I said, I'm not a child! You behave like one, she says, an then she relented. All right, she says, eleven. Not a minute longer.

Well, it spoilt my evening. I mean, you can't enjoy yourself, can yer? Not with a threat like that hanging over yer head. Well, I'm trying to listen to Arthur, an keeping an eye on me watch. I mean, she wouldn't do it, she wouldn't dare, but at the same time... An then I hear what it is Arthur's saying.

Have you give it any thought? he says. What? I says. Like what I've been saying, he says, getting together with her, like tying the knot with her. What, marry her, you mean? I wouldn't put it out of your mind, he says. What, Mrs Hollingbery? I says. A woman can be very handy, he says, about the house I mean... I mean, she can still get about the house, can't she? You know, he goes on, cooking an cleaning, all that sort of thing. Yer, he goes on, from what I've seen of her she seems to have a few years in her yet, an the old roast beef an Yorkshire on Sundays, the odd meat pudding, pies, an other creature comforts – I mean, they're not to be sneezed at, Alf. Yer, I says, but I dunno if she'd suit me though, Arthur – looking at me watch.

You don't have to love a woman to marry her, he says. You take yer upper classes, yer aristocracy, them people don't marry for love. Position, that's all they marry for. That's all they're interested in. Joining the dynasties, putting two large fortunes together. You marry Mrs Hollingbery, he says, an you'll be doing the same, using yer loaf, putting two pensions together. Course, he says, you'd have to give her her jugals... but her age you'd probably only be called on about once a week, an you could manage that, eh? An from what young Marigold tells me you seem to be hitting it off all right with her. As he been talking about me? I says. No, of course not, Arthur says. No, no, of course not. But from what he says you seem to be getting along all right with her. Getting along all right? Oh yer, I thought, hitting it off with her! You got the right time, Arthur? I says looking at my watch, I think I've stopped. Yer, Arthur says, getting his watch out, it's a quarter to eleven.

Gawd! Talk about bloody Cinderella ... I gotta go, I said, finishing me beer off. Hey, what's the hurry? he shouts after me, they don't shut here for another fifteen minutes ... But I'm gone. I can't hear him. I'm off. Gawd almighty, annit marvellous? I'm under the cosh an I'm not even married to her! The bloody town hall clock strikes eleven as I run past it. Oh gawd! She wouldn't. She wouldn't dare!

But she did. I gets home an I'm bolted out. I banged an knocked on that bloody door fit to wake the dead. But nothing. Not from her, anyway. A few neighbours shouted out but I gave them a mouthful. An then it started to bloody rain. I tried to shelter in the porch but I was getting soaked ... an cold. It's supposed to be summer but it was perishing. I thought, I'll catch me death here. An then I thought – I know what I'll do, I'll go over an knock the Johnsons up. They're decent neighbours. They won't mind. They let me use their phone sometimes. Well, after a while (well, they're sound asleep an it takes me a while to wake em up ...) I hear sounds of life an a light comes on, an I hear Fred Johnson. Who is it? he says. It's me, I says, Mr Garnett. Open up. Something awful's happened. He opens his door an I step in. What is it? he says. I'm glad you were up, I says. I was in bed, he says following me into his living room. What's wrong? he says. Mrs Hollingbery's taken sleeping tablets, I says.

Good God! he says, picking up his phone an dialling. I'll phone for ambulance. Then Mrs Johnson calls out from upstairs, Who is it? she calls. It's Mr Garnett, Fred calls up to her. What's he want this time of night, she shouts.

Mrs Hollingbery's swallowed sleeping tablets, he calls out to her. Oh dear, she shouts, poor woman. Phone the ambulance. I'm phoning the ambulance, shouts Fred.

Well, I'm just pouring meself a whisky to take the chill out of me bones – got a little cocktail cabinet Fred has – when Mrs Johnson pops her head round the living-room door. She's in her curlers an dressing gown an twitching with panic. Phone the ambulance, she says to Fred, I'll see what I can do over there, I used to be a nurse – an she's gone, out the front door and across the road to see if she can help Mrs Hollingbery. Except she can't get in, an she don't give me time to tell her that . . .

Where's she gone? I says to Fred. But he don't wanna talk to me either. He's too taken up with the excitement of everything, an shushes me an says, Come on, come on, into the phone. Come on . . . Hello? Are they all asleep? She's gone over to help, he says to me, see what she can do, she's studied first aid. Then into the phone again: Hello? Come on, come on . . . Hello? Ah . . . Ambulance, please. Yes. Ambulance! Of course it's serious! Yes, very urgent. Yes. Fools! Yes. Attempted suicide. Yes. Sleeping tablets. Er, just a minute, an he turns to me. How many did she take? he asks me. One, I says. One, he says, into the phone. Then he turns to me. Did you say one? Yes, I says. Well, if looks could kill . . . Er, I'm sorry, he says into the phone, I'm afraid there's been some mistake . . . I'm sorry . . . I . . . I said I was sorry, he shouts, an slams the phone down.

Why didn't you say she only took one? he says. One's not dangerous. I know it's not, I said. You said something awful had happened, he says – he's really annoyed now. Well, something awful *has* happened, I says, she's taken a sleeping tablet an she's locked me out an I can't get in cos I can't wake her up an it's raining. An you woke me up to tell me that? he says. Well, I says, I knew you wouldn't mind, cos you're a good neighbour, not like some of em down this street, an besides, we're friends. No, no, no, we're not, he says. We're not friends. Course we are, I says, course we're friends. You don't realize what a good friend you are. I tell you, I said, there's not many would do for me what you're doing for me tonight. Doing for you? What am I doing for you? he says. Letting me sleep here, I says. You're not sleeping here, he says. Oh I can sleep anywhere, I says, this sofa'll do me. I'm not fussy. I'll be all right here, I said, settling meself down.

An then the knocking on his front door starts . . . very loud it is. What's that? I says, is that the ambulance? An then, of course, Fred realizes. It's my wife, he says, an runs to let her in. But of course, Mrs Johnson still don't know what's happened and thinks Mrs Hollingbery is dying across the road (which if it was true wouldn't bother me, to be honest), and before Fred can explain things to her, she's grabbed him by the arm and dragged him out into the rain with her, shouting at him in her panic, Hurry up! Quick! Hurry up! I can't get in to Mrs Hollingbery. See if you can do anything. It's all right, Fred tries to tell her. It's not all right, Mrs Johnson screams at him, that poor woman!!

Well, I don't hear all this because I'm fast asleep by now, an when I'm asleep it takes a lot to wake me up, specially after a few beers – an I'd had a few – an also what I don't know is that their front door has shut on em an they can't get in, an they ain't got much of a porch . . .

They had a few words with me in the morning, though, when they finally got back in. But as I tried to explain to them, it wasn't my fault.

Mrs Hollingbery – I can't let her win, I mustn't let her get the upper hand.

6

I was over at the corner shop the other day, it's a Paki runs it now, a Mr Kittel, an I must say in all fairness to him, I mean, him being an alien an all that, he is running it a bit better than old Mr Williams used to run it. He was all right old Williams, but he should never have got himself involved in a corner shop. He's Welsh you see, an of course he had no head for figures. There's not much counting to do in a corner shop but it's still a bit too much for a Welsh brain. My Rita always felt sorry for him (as I've said before, she was always sorry for the underdog) an I remember her saying about old Williams once, she said, I feel sorry for him, cos he's a dying race. What're you talking about? I said, I know he's Welsh, but he's still British, an they've got us to look after em. I'm talking about his living, she said, the corner shopkeeper. They're dying out. They're being absorbed by the big supermarkets. It's progress, she says, but you can still feel sorry for him.

Supermarket! Progress? Don't talk daft, I said. That's not progress. It is progress, she says, I mean, blimey, even you can't argue with that. How's it progress then? I said. Well of course it is, she says, it's a more efficient means of distribution, isn't it? Efficient? I said, what're you talking about, efficient? I mean, blimey, your supermarket is a prime example of your bloody Labour inefficiency, if you ask me. You're potty, she says. Never mind about potty, I says, I mean, you go in them places, yer supermarkets, an you've got to bloody serve yourself, haven't you? Eh? They don't attempt to serve you, do they? Oh no. I mean, you're working for *them*. All they want to do is sit by the till on their backsides an take your money.

But that is more efficient, she says, it's modern methods. Modern methods? I said. An it's quicker, she says, an better service. Better service? I says. Quicker? Blimey! What're you talking about? I mean, you buy one thing, if you can manage to find it, an then the next thing you want is miles away, at the end of the shop! Oh I see, says Rita, I suppose you want to stay with Mr Williams and the corner shop, do you? Yer, well, I said, I had to say it, what's wrong with it? It's handy, Else says. What's wrong with it? It's bloody filthy, Rita says, for a start. That's what's wrong with it!

Oh yer? I says. Well one thing about Mr Williams, I said, you can get a bit of tick there. I mean, if you're an old age pensioner you can get a bit of credit. But I mean, you go up your supermarket an try an get a dozen eggs on the slate till Friday an see what they say! Or a packet of tea, Else says. Mr Williams' shop! It's awful in there, Rita says. Awful? What're you talking about awful, I says. It's not hygienic, Rita says, that's what I'm talking about. Flies, there are flies all over his bacon. Flies? I said. A few flies won't hurt you, my dear, will they? At least his bacon's gotta bit of taste, annit? He brushes the flies off it, Else says, he don't let em stay on it.

Look, you go to the supermarket, Rita says, an everything is under cover, and the bacon is hermetically sealed, in hygienic plastic bags. So it might be, I said, so it might be, but your mother goes up there, she goes up there an buys it, an she brings it home, an she opens it, she undoes your hermeygenic seals, an *then* the flies get on it! They'd be our flies though, Else says. What're you talking about, I says, you silly moo! Our flies! It don't matter whose bloody flies they are, do it? Well, if they're our flies, Else says, at least we know where they've been, don't we? What're you talking about? Silly moo! Our flies! They could be anybody's flies, couldn't they? They could be next door's flies for all we know. And who knows where they've been? I mean, blimey, you can't have your own bloody flies! Flies ain't like mice. You can have your own mice, but you can't have your own bloody flies. I mean, they're too mobile, flies, ain't they? They come in through windows. Them mice are not ours anyway, Else says. Not the point, I says. They come in from next door too, she says. Well, you can't blame em, can you, I said. You leave too much out for em. I mean, blimey, the way you carry on, it's a wonder we ain't got every mouse in the street living here. Bloody welfare state for mice this house is. Look, Else says, if you blocked the holes up they couldn't get in. An if you kept the house a bit neat an tidy, I told her, an put things away proper, they wouldn't want to! Pig! she says to me. Ah well, I miss her though, she was a good woman.

Anyway, as I was saying the corner shop is a lot better now since the Paki's been running it. You have to say it, you can't odds it, yer Paki is brighter than yer Welsh ... Anyway, I walk into the corner shop an Marigold's in there leaning on the counter. Hello, Mr Garnett, Mr Kittel says, hello. I am just saying to Marigold ... Hey man, says Marigold, less of the Marigold, eh? *Winston* if you don't mind, Gunga Din. Mr Garnett, the Paki says, I am very sorry to hear of the loss of your wonderful good lady, a sorry business. Yer, well, I says, it happens to all of us. Oh yes, but it was a very sad loss to me, he says. It's a sad loss to *me*, I says. Oh yes, oh yes, he says, but I have lost a very good customer. An I've lost a good wife, I says. Oh yes, oh yes, he says, but it was a bad blow to me, her going like that, so sudden, you see. It was a bad blow for me, I said. Oh yes, very bad blow, but it has done me no good her going like that, he said, so sudden. What d'you mean? says Marigold. Well, she went owing me a few pounds, says Mr Kittel. Well, that's a nice thing to say, says Marigold. I am not saying anything, says Mr Kittel. Not saying anything? says Marigold. Bringing that up, maligning the woman now she's gone? I am not maligning her, says Mr Kittel, all I have said, she went owing me a few pounds, that's all I have said. Well, she couldn't help it, says Marigold, I mean, blimey, it's not her fault she went, is it? I am not saying that, says Mr Kittel, all I am saying, if Mrs Garnett had gone on Saturday instead of Wednesday I'd be all right, because, you see, she always paid me Friday.

Look, I don't suppose she wanted to go on Wednesday, I said. I mean, blimey, if she'd had her way, she'd have preferred to wait till Saturday. Or even longer, says Marigold. Look, I said, if I'd had my way she wouldn't have gone at all. I don't know what you're bloody moaning about, I says, I'm the one should be moaning, I'm the one she's left in the mess, with that bloody thing upstairs, you don't think she went on a Wednesday just to do you out of money, do you? I am not saying that, says Mr Kittel, I am just saying it has cost me money. It's cost *me* money, I said. It's cost me her pension an the money she got for sitting in that wheelchair. Yes, yes, I am sure, he says, but her going Wednesday is not good for me. It is just my luck. Just your luck? I says. What about my bloody luck? What about her luck? I am not blaming her, Mr Kittel says, Mrs Garnett was a good customer and good payer, all I am saying ... he knows, he says, pointing to Marigold, he comes into my shop. He takes groceries. Put them on slate, Mrs Garnett will pay later, he says.

And she did, Marigold says, she always paid you. Not

now! She cannot pay me now, Sambo, Mr Kittel bawls at
Marigold, that is what I am saying. He orders. Marigold
orders. Put on slate. Put on slate ... put on slate ... and
then she passes on. Well, that's not my fault, is it? I said. I
am not saying it is your fault, he says. Well what are you
tellin me for? I says. How much does Mr Garnett owe
you? says Marigold. Me? I says, I owe him nothing. Just
this tobacco I'm buying. Well, says Marigold, what Mrs
Garnett owed. What Mrs Garnett owed? I tell him, Mrs
Garnett owed! I am thinking this will happen, Mr Kittel
says.

Look, I said, it's all right you saying my wife owed you
money, but where's your proof? I mean, any old Tom,
Dick or Harry can come knocking on your door saying
your wife owes em money, specially when she's gone an
not here to deny it to their face. What proof you got? Eh?
Bills, John John. I wanna see bills, signed bills an
statements, John John. Signed statements with signa-
tures on em, John John. That's how we do business in
England. Not on hearsay, John John. I'm taking my
custom elsewhere from now on! From now on I buy
British!! An I walked out. An as I'm going he calls out: An
what d'you think I am, bleeding Japanese? They soon
pick up our ways, don't they?

An then of course, there was the milkman. She went
owing him money too. He comes knocking on the door.
Ah, I've been trying to catch you he says. Oh yer, I says,
an what are you trying to catch me for? Look, if it's
money, I said. Whoa, keep your hair on, he says. Don't be
fakesshus I says. Well, there is a bit of settling up to do,
he says. Gordon Bennett, I says, more debts she's left I
spose?

Well, she couldn't pay me when she was in hospital, he
says, an then I went off on me holidays. But never mind,
he says, I wasn't worried. You wasn't worried? I says.
No, I knew it'd be all right, he says. You knew it'd be all

right, I says. Yer, he says, it didn't worry me a bit ... Now let's see, he says, opening his book up, there's the milk ... butter ... eggs ... sugar an tea she had ... and a few bets that went down. A few bets? I said. Marvellous annit? Gambling to the end! One big bet she had, he said, quite a punter your old lady was, I'll miss her, he says. Yer, I says, an so will the bookies! It was horse at Newmarket, he says, she really fancied it, said it reminded her of you. A real outsider it was, he says, at sixty to one. She put five pounds on it to win. What a punter! An I could hear the admiration in his voice.

Five pounds at sixty to one? I says. I'm shocked. I mean, the silly moo! She was scared you'd find out, he says. Well, I have an I? I said, too bloody late! You'd have stopped it, would you? he says. Of course I'd have bloody well stopped it, I said. Bad enough running up bills without bloody gambling debts! Women! They beggar you! They got their women libs, what about our man's lib? Every debt they like to run up the man is responsible for! What are we, their keepers? They take away yer reins to control em with an when they gallop off spending all yer money, we're held responsible! They ought to have left that Mrs Pankhurst chained to the railings! I'm gonna appeal. I'm gonna appeal to yer European courts, that's what I'll do. When I married her a woman's place was in the home, an she was only allowed to spend what her husband chose to give her, that was the contract ...

It won, he said. Eh? I said. It won, he said. Three hundred pounds, an he started to count it out. Well, I was speechless. D'you know what the horse was called? he says. I shook my head. 'Chauvinist Pig', he said. But I didn't care. Cor! What a party I had. I even invited Mrs Hollingbery.

7

See, here's a thing that annoys me about yer telly an the people who run it. The other night they put on the story of Edward the Eighth, Prince of Wales an Duke of Windsor to be, God rest him. But they didn't have their facts right. You see, Edward, Teddy as we called him, wanted to marry an American girl – they got that bit right, Mrs Simpson. An she'd been divorced – they had that bit right too. But Teddy wasn't bothered. Probably didn't even fancy her if the truth is known, but he saw his duty to England, he knew where the money was. The Americans would have give a lot to have one of their own on the throne of England. Well, sharing the throne, an Teddy saw that by marrying an American, it would have been a way of getting money off yer Yanks and into the Bank of England. I mean, he would've charged em a fair bit. Probably have become Emperor of America an all, and got the Colony back for us! We should never have given it away really. Well, I mean, they was under us in the old days wasn't they, the Yanks? Spoke the same language as us, didn't they? Buggered it up a bit but, I mean, they was part of the British Empire see; but they wanted to be independent, start up on their own. So they come to us like a son might go to his father and said, Daddy, they said, we're grown up now... get married... have a place of our own. And England, in her infinite wisdom said, So be it my son. Yes you may. And they been a credit ain't they? Done better than any of the other Colonies. Done better than Canada, Australia, India, well, I mean, everyone's done better than India, ain't they? Well, I admit we helped them, didn't we? Sent some of our best people out there to get em started, didn't we? I mean, no, it's true. When they was struggling, when they was short of labour, who was it flogged them all their coons? They was our coons. They came out of our Africa. I mean, it's facts. We had, like, a surplus of coons see, all lolling about in Africa doing nuffing, swinging in the bleeding trees, and we exported them. Exported what we didn't want to America. I'll bet if the truth was known, they wouldn't mind shipping them all back here again. But we don't want them see, cos we've got enough of our own.

Trouble with this country is the bloody Common Market. Daft idea that is, Common Market. Should have refused to join till they made the Queen Emperor of Europe. I mean, now they brought it in there's thousands of bloody foreigners swarming to this bloody country without even having to have passports even. We've got millions of Eyeties and Krauts, Froggies, Spagnolies, Brussel Sprouts. All coming in here taking our jobs off us, ain't they? So we're going to have to go over to the Continent of Europe looking for work, ain't we? Be bloody confusing when another war breaks out. I mean you won't know what side you're on, will yer? Going to be thousands of boats taking people backwards and forwards so that they can join up with their own armies before they can even start the bloody war. See, old Enoch Powell, he had the right idea. People should stay in their own countries, the countries which was allocated to them. The countries we put em all in when we run the world, when we had our Empire, before the bloody Labour Party give it all away.

Most of us in London can trace our kin back to Drake an sailing with him. All right, so he might have sailed from Plymouth, nobody's saying he didn't. But he preferred Tilbury, cos Tilbury was nearer to London an that's where he wanted to be, cos he looked on London as his home. He only played bowls at Plymouth. He might have been born there, in Devon, but he soon moved to London. Once he knew he had it in him to be a great Admiral he moved to London, cos he knew that only in London would he be able to realize his ambitions. I know they've got water at Devon, but it was no use attacking Devon, was it? Not in them days. The Spanish wasn't after Devon – a few bloody fields an a couple of shepherds. They was after London cos outside of London there was nothing worth having – not in them days . . . there still ain't. All the wealth of England is in London. When Drake was sailing the Main the people of London had no use for miners digging an farmers farming bits of fields. Let others dig up the treasures an farm the fields, then Drake an his lads would nick it off em on the high seas. Blimey, the shops of London was full of stuff in them days. Good days they was, when England was mighty an we controlled the seas an anything we found on em was ours. They had values then. They believed in the Ten Commandments. Thou shalt not steal. An if you did, they strung you up. Now, blimey, get caught stealing now an all they do is bung you in prison, keep you at the expense of the rest of us, an then after a few years, let you out so you steal again. Cut their hand off, I say. Take my word. Look, you let a man steal an get away with it, an before you know where you are it's habit, an some habits are hard to break.

Anyway, my father knew the Prince of Wales very well. They was mates. They used to go out drinking together. That old Prince was down the East End regular he was. He used to drink at the Royal Crown with my dad. It's how it got its Royal.

He was a bit of a boozer – he liked his pint. He could drink a yard of ale in ten seconds the old Prince could. I tell you, the only man in the whole of England who could beat him drinking was my father. I've seen em together. I was only a little kid an I had to go up the pub to tell my dad his dinner was ready, an there they was the two of em – my dad an the Prince of Wales. His Royal Highness leaning up against the bar he was, an the Prince of Wales had his arm round my dad's shoulder an laughing he was at something my dad was telling him – some joke about Baldwin I spose – I can see em now, the Prince of Wales laughing an saying to my dad, you're the wittiest man I know, Alfred, you're wittier than Oscar Wilde. He's a pufta, my old man said. An the old Prince said, he ain't the only one, Alf, why d'you think I walk about with my hands behind me back? What, protecting yer royal rear? my dad says. Yes, he says, an they fell about laughing.

They was such good friends them two. They used to go to football together, down to West Ham. Cos it's yer Royal team, the old claret an blues, Henry the Eighth's old team, when he used to court Anne Boleyn down at Boleyn Castle. It was him picked their colours. The claret for his favourite wine, an the blue for yer royal blood. You see, as the Prince of Wales told my father, it was at West Ham where Henry the Eighth met Anne Boleyn, cos she was a local girl. But she was untrue to him an started to muck about with someone else, so he chopped her head off. He was heard to say to her down at West Ham one day, he said, I'm telling you, Anne, I'm giving you fair warning, if I catch you at it with anyone else, I'll give the lads your head to kick off with. I'll bung

My dad, trying to catch the Prince's eye to let him know
they've been open ten minutes already.

it on the centre spot next home game. An he did. An that is why today you get the custom of spinning the coin. Heads kick off first.

Yes, he was a great fan of West Ham the old Prince, an no matter where that man was while he was alive, no matter what part of the world he was in, every Saturday night he would rush out an buy an English evening paper, an turn straight to the sports page to see how West Ham had got on. That's the sort of man he was. The best King we ever had. An he would've stayed King too if it hadn't been for that bloody Baldwin.

I remember one day, my old dad coming in, tears in his eyes he had, an he said, I've just seen Teddy up the pub. Come down special to see me he did, said my dad, an apparently, what happened, King Edward, as he was then, come into the pub, put his arm round my dad's shoulder an with tears in his eyes, said to my dad, Alfred, he said, they're trying to send me away. Who are? my dad says. An the King says, Baldwin an the rest of his bloody cabinet. You see, as my dad said, it was nothing to do with Mrs Simpson at all, it was political chicanery. Old King Edward was too friendly with the workers, an Baldwin didn't like him hob-nobbing down here in the East End with em. Yer, the greatest King we ever had he was. 'The Worker's King' they called him.

After that night I'm talking about, my dad didn't see the King for a few weeks, an he got a bit worried, an so he phoned up the Palace an asked to speak with the King, an one of them equerries answered the phone. An my dad said to him: Listen, toffee-nose, I want to speak to His Majesty. An they wouldn't put him through. So my dad said, we're all lined up here at Wapping, he said, an ready to march, so if you harm one hair of that man's head, we'll have the lot of you. An they would too, all them dockers, cos they was men in them days – before their unions corrupted em!

My dad and the Duke off to West Ham. They're in the front
car. Three points off the League Championships that year
we were and Wembley and the White Horse looming in sight.
The old Duke said that day in the car going down to West
Ham, he turned to my father and he said, Alfred, he said, if
West Ham win the double this year all the drinks in the East
End are on me. An he meant it! We won the Cup but we lost
the League – kicked out of it we was – that's when your
football violence started rearing its ugly head in yer North.
Look at them cars! Makes yer heart bleed with pride. Nothing
like yer Japanese rubbish, are they? They didn't have to
worry about petrol economy in those days because we
owned all the oil in the world. An what we didn't own, only
had to send a gunboat an we didn't argue too much about
the price. That's in the old days when yer Navy, like Drake's
Navy, showed a profit.

My dad's team.

You see, when you were paying em £12 maximum, you could afford to have more players. In fact, you had more directors. Most of the directors brought their boots in those days in case they were asked to play. Jim Barrett. Eight pints he'd have in the Barking Arms before the kick-off. None of yer modern training rubbish for him. If he didn't like the referee's decision he used to kick the ball clean out of the stand. If you look close you'll see the Prince of Wales there.

8

Anyway, to get back to the beginning. God made the world in seven days, the whole world – England, America, Russia, China, not counting all the stars and things – an the moon an the sun. Made em all in the same week HE did. Blimey, HE didn't hang about, must have been hard at it all week, not like some of the rubbish you got now – in the bog smoking all day. And HE made Adam, and HE took a rib from him and made Eve so she could clean and wash up and look after Adam's house for him – sort of home help. And what's your bloody Darwin got to say about that? Cos there it is, annit, in black and white in the Good Book. So we wasn't monkeys. An it says in here we was made by God in HIS own image.

You mean God looks like you? Marigold says. I don't mean exact resemblance, what I mean is HE made us perfect like Himself, I says. *You? Perfect? says Marigold.

I don't mean perfect – that way, I says. I mean, I got faults, I know that. What I mean is – perfect in build and shape. Look at that hand! Here you are, I says, showing him the other one. HE made us with four fingers and one thumb on each hand. Even thought of that, *two* hands. And HE puts them on the end of yer arms where they're most handy – why they called em hands, I suppose. And HE give us a nose and ears to hang your glasses on. The Lord made us and the world and HE made everything in the world perfect for us, cos being God HE knew the kind of world we'd like. And all the food we'd like to eat. Like your cows which turn themselves into beef. And yer pig and your lamb, and all the veg to go with it. And HE made yer fish.

And your chips, says Marigold. Yes, I says, and your chips, and your salt and your vinegar, smart arse! An with your cow HE give us milk for our tea as well. All in the same animal, with your beef. An HE made everyone the same religion – Christians. An that's how it was for years. Everyone happy, all believing in the same thing until HIM and Lucifer, who was like sort of a second in command to God up there – HIS oppo – like yer David Steel is to yer Owen, yer Thatcher is to yer Tebbit, and yer Kinnock to yer Hattersley – until they fell out.

Cobblers, says Marigold. An God chucked Lucifer out of Heaven, I said, like I'm going to chuck you out of this bleedin house in a minute if you don't shut up. Blimey, you made me lose me thread now.

Lucifer was relegated, says Marigold. Right! I says, but like all losers, Lucifer was after revenge and went about trying to turn people off God, an some listened, an that's why HE sent yer Christ down here to try an reform em and bring em back to the true path, and that's how you get yer bloody Christmas. Funny thing about God – yer Micks think yer God is Irish, your Ikey thinks HE's Jewish . . .

He is, said Marigold. He started the Christian religion in a Jewish ghetto in the Arab quarter of Bethlehem.

Look, he might have started as a Jew, I says, but he soon learned the error of his ways. Don't get me wrong, I've got nothing personal against yer Jews. I mean . . . some of em's all right. Yer Max Miller, Maxie Bygraves, Max Wall, Issy Bonn. You – reading this book – are you of Jewish persuasion? Well, if you are, who persuaded you? I bet you didn't buy this book. I bet you borrowed it out of the library or off some Christian friend who bought it, eh, Ikey? I mean – just having a little joke . . . I got nothing against em personal. But you got to admit, it was a big mistake killing Jesus. Bound to put people's backs up. An calling him King of the Jews, our Lord Jesus, and therefore inferring that his father was Jewish. I mean, God ain't Jewish – don't even look Jewish. God's Church of England . . . that's the last thing HE would have made hisself. Her Majesty the Queen's Church . . . only got to look at pictures of HIM to see that. I'll tell you God's nationality, what country HE has on HIS passport . . .

Not England! shouts Marigold.

Yes, England! I says. Look, yer Mary and yer Joseph are the first two English names to appear in yer Bible, right? And what can be more English than Mary and Joseph? Mary Poppins . . . and . . . er . . . Joe . . . Joe Lyons . . . Couldn't be more English. Anyway, Joseph wasn't even Jesus's father, see.

God used to come down here a bit more in the old days, cos HE liked this world. It was one of the best worlds HE ever made. Had a friend here, Joseph, who had a girlfriend, Mary. Well, they was engaged and he introduced her to God who was a good-looking man. Well, HE'd have been daft to have made himself ugly, wouldn't HE? Turned her head. I mean, you don't meet God every day, do yer? Turn any girl's head. Well, he was better looking than any of yer pop stars. And I mean, being a virile man, well, boom, boom, they couples, an HE's give her one. Look, you don't believe me? I says to Marigold, it's in the book, in yer Bible! Course I always keep it handy cos you never know.

These are the facts, what yer actual Bible says. 'Now the birth of Christ was on this wise: When as his mother

Mary was espoused to Joseph, before they came together, she was found with child of the Holy Ghost. Then Joseph her husband, being a just man, and not willing to make her a public example, was minded to put her away privily. But while he thought on these things, behold, the Angel of the Lord appeared unto him in a dream, saying, Joseph, thou son of David, fear not to take unto thee Mary thy wife; for that which is conceived in her is of the Holy Ghost.'

Holy Ghost! In them days that was just a phrase for saying that a girl had dropped for one. Like had been, you know . . . we say, Hello, she's got one in the oven. So in them days, when a girl, like, dropped for one they used to say, Hello, I see the Holy Ghost's been there, eh? An Joseph knew that. But God came to Joseph an said, I'm sorry and I apologize, but we're only human, an I can't afford no scandal – cos they had their Mary Whitehouses in them days too, I suppose – so do me a favour, be a mate, say nothing, look after the kid, an I'll see you all right up in Heaven. An Joseph said, So be it, cos he loved God – don't we all? So he stayed shtum, married the girl, brought up the boy proper – in the carpentry business, making wooden crosses, cos God wanted the lad to start at the bottom an work his way up.

An that's the last we would have heard about it, an nobody would have known that Jesus was in actual fact the Son of God, but for him – that monkey Matthew – blabbing. Big mouth. Cos he was a mole, a sneak, the Nigel Dempster of his day who you daren't tell anything to unless you want it all round the neighbourhood. An of course he had to go an blab it all for a few pieces of silver. Course, once he started they all jumped on the bandwagon: Mark, John, Paul Callan, Nigel Dempster. Anyway, the reason why HE sent them to Bethlehem and not London is quite simple, annit? Eh? (Well, here you are – here's a little puzzle for you. Get your crossword brain going on this.) I'll give you a clue: Bethlehem's in the Middle East. You got it yet? OIL! See, if you're going to run the world you need oil. Raw materials. God ain't daft. Cos HE wanted us, the English, HIS chosen people, to run the world – HIS world.

Course it wasn't until God showed us how to make motor cars and airplanes an things that oil became valuable. And then HE showed us how to get the oil out of the ground. HE didn't show the Arabs. HE didn't show the Japs how to make cars either – they nicked that off us. US! *We're* the ones HE showed. HIS chosen people. And then yer Jews had to go and mess it up.

A few years ago, see, yer Arabs was happy with their desert an their flies and filth, an we could have all the oil we wanted for next to nothing – just for a few beads, bits of broken glass. But your Jews have to go out there. They have to move in next door to em, with their cars and their fur coats and their big cigars, an before you know where you are – before you can say Moyshe Dayan – your Arab is unsettled and wants the same. *He* wants a big car now, and a fur coat and a big cigar. He's not happy with his camel now he ain't. An we've got to pay through the nose for his bleedin oil. Anyway, that's why HE sent em to Bethlehem.

Course, trouble is, you've got so many religions now, you don't know where you are. Today, every Tom, Dick an Harry's got his own religion. They can't all be right, can they? I mean, according to yer Book there's only one true one. So the rest of em's lying, ain't they? Belong to yer own, they say! It's not a question of your own is it, eh? It's a question of HIS, annit? What one does HE belong to? HIM, HIM up there, yer God. That's the one you got to belong to. No good belonging to any of the others.

But who knows which one is HIS? I mean, that's your problem, and God ain't said nothing for years, HE ain't.

Trouble is, you can belong to a religion all your life, support it properly, give money to it, go to its dances, go to its bazaars, buy its raffle tickets, and when you die, get up there and find out it was the wrong one, and the one round the corner was the right one or something. I mean that's what's so perplexing for all of us mortals down here. Well, I mean, if your religion ain't going to help you get into Heaven, you might as well have the extra hour in bed Sunday morning.

But never mind – God will get HIS own back on em. HE'll get his revenge. HE will send down a scourge upon them – a plague – a pestilence – an he has an all – in the shape of yer Aids, yer herpes and yer Rt Hon Wedgie Benn Esquire. Bloody Wedgie Benn. He don't know what side his bread's buttered. I mean, he talks like one of us, and acts like one of them. He talks like a Tory I mean, sounds like one. I mean, he was born with a silver spoon in his mouth, a natural born Lord, wasn't he? And spends all his time attacking his own people, the people he was brought up with, boys he went to school with, and trying to take away their big houses and nationalizing their factories. Blimey, if they'd had any sense, his parents, they'd have smothered him at birth.

See, what they ought to do is let all of us Tories live one end of the country, and all your Labour up the other end, so when the revolution starts we'll all know where are are. I'm behind the enemy lines here. I ought to be in Virginia Water with me own kind.

Anyway, I don't want to depress meself talking about Wedgie Benn. Things is black enough as they are. An when I say black I mean bloody black! I mean, people say I don't like em, but blimey, they don't like each other ... except as food! At least while they was cannibals, while they was eating each other, at least they was keeping themselves down. Now they've stopped eating each other, they'll want to start eating all our lamb an beef, an pig an things an next thing before you know it, it's boom, boom, an what have you got? A bloody world food shortage!

I don't mind a few of em over here, a few like Marigold, mucking out, home helping an that, you know, working on our railways for us, an our buses, looking after our public conveniences an emptying bedpans. Doing in fact what Enoch brought em over to do in the first place, and at an economical price – cheap labour, in fact! Everything was all right until the bloody unions had to poke their nose into it.

Bloody unions!

The unions are running the country now, they say. Well, it ain't our union, not the one I belonged to before I retired. That bloody union had no say at all. Well, look what happened to us. The last strike we had, before I retired. We was out for months we was. Months! We run out of employment, we run out of assistance. So I got all the middle-of-the-road ones, the moderates like, together an I said, enough's enough. I said, we've shown em our power, now let's go back. So we did, an the bloody place wasn't there no more. They'd shut it up. Closed it down an buggered off. Everything was gone. It had bills up, FOR SALE plastered all over it. So I'm redundant, pensioned OFF!

Me! Fought in two wars I did. I mean, Dunkirk – I was one of the last to leave I was. I could have been one of the first, but I said no, no, I said, I'm a sergeant – I could have been an officer but I wanted to stay with the lads. I said, I'm a sergeant, get the other lads off first, I said. Blimey, I copped a blighty one there, didn't I?

See, I was holding this grenade see, and the Captain, God rest his soul, he kept saying: Throw it now, Garnett, throw it for God's sake. And I kept saying: No, Captain, no, let me get nearer to them – to the enemy. An I waited, see, an I waited, and me mates all round me

103

They were at it even then. London burning above our heads
and no smoking in the tube. Bloody fools!

When we had bombs dropped on us in the Blitz.
When Jerry was bombing us, some of them filed in orderly
fashion down the tube, singing songs, brewing up and
playing accordions. But most of us was defiant, defiant of
anything the Hun could do. We wouldn't let no foreigners
drive us underground. I'm not bigoted but yer bloody Japs,
they're totally lacking in moral fibre they are. One titchy little
atom bomb on them, one atom bomb an they come out
crying with their hands up. That's the difference. We was
only just trying it out, wasn't we? Got to see how it worked.
Can't expect em to spend all that money making it an not try
it out. Anyway, we should have dropped a few more on em.
That would have buggered up their car trade for em.

was quaking in fear that it would go off before I'd thrown it. An the Captain kept saying: Throw it, for Gawd's sake, throw it, Alf. But I waited – and I finally threw it among em, and they was so close, I almost took me hand off with it. Hanging by a thread it was. Blood! Blood was terrible. The men around me – all me mates – soldiers all of them, was keeling over at the sight of it. But, I mean, it's all right now – could split a plank with it. I mean, it's an example of one of the wonders of plastic surgery. But what thanks do you get? Thrown on the scrap heap!

9

You know what the trouble is, Else says to me one day, just before she passed on. It's all the cutbacks. It's your Mrs Thatcher, she don't like lame dogs, she wants everyone to stand on their own feet, she said.

Shurrup about Mrs Thatcher, I said. Never mind, she says, perhaps Labour will win the next election an that nice Mr Kinnock will spend more money on the Health Service...

Labour! I said. Looking after theirselves, that's what they'll be doing. Feathering his own nest, that's what your nice Mr Kinnock'll be doing. Like that nice Mr Wilson done an that nice Mr Callaghan. They both did better under Labour... but nobody else did! Bloody darling Harold Wilson was flogging peerages to anybody with hundred thousand pounds to spare!

Ted Heath got a boat, Else says. Yes, I says, an bloody Michael Foot was after a new coat but he didn't get it. They're all the same, I said. They're all in it for theirselves... Blimey, becoming Prime Minister is better than winning the pools it is. An we can't even get a powered wheelchair. Bloody Labour Party! Blimey, when they first came to power they didn't have nothing, none of em! Not even a pot to piss in. Now look at em... they sit in that Parliament up there, copping their thirty or forty thousand a year an they don't do nothing for nobody...

107

Darling Harold made a packet out of betting on an election. How did he do it? Obvious annit? It's obvious when you think about it. You see, they wasn't only betting on who'd win the election, but when it would be. An the only man in the country who knew when it would be was old Wilson, cos it was him what had to choose when it would be. And before he made it official, he went to see Her Majesty up the Palace, which was his prerogative, an he said to her, Can I absolve the Parliament? An she said, So be it. An she's hardly got her crown off when he was out the back door and down the betting shop bunging his money on. And what's more, he didn't have the grace to bung a few quid on for her, or Philip, an that's the kind of man yer Harold Wilson was!

They don't get forty thousand a year, Else says. All right, they may not admit to getting it, I says. I mean, what they tell us they get an what they bung in their pockets is two different things. Perks, my dear, perks. That's what it is, I says, that's where the real money is. Ones! Nelsons! Cash in their pockets, no questions asked, it stands to reason, dunnit? You can't tell me them Labourites can afford to live up there the way they do, mixing with yer hoi poloi on what they're supposed to be earning? They ain't got nothing of their own, no private fortunes, not like yer Tories have. Look at em, them an the bloody SDP, all living in five hundred thousand pound penthouses in yer Royal Borough of Wapping...

Wapping's not a Royal Borough says Else. It will be now they're all living there, says I. Get rid of us, condemn our houses, clear us out an then build penthouses for theirselves! They didn't have any money to spare improving our houses when we lived there, but they soon found the money for theirselves, didn't they? Course, it's near yer Parliament, annit? I spose one of em looked out the window... thought, that'd be handy place to live, yer Wapping. Get them lot out what's living there, get em all evicted, smarten it up. Very adjacent that'll be. Won't need a telephone even, just shout across – you know how water carries – anything doing over there today? Right. Nothing on. I'll have a lay-in.

You shouldn't let it worry you, says Else. Look, I says, I've served under eleven Prime Ministers an I've been poor under every one of em. Bloody politicians! Look, I says, everyone's got to get a living, all right, I admit that. I don't mind someone making a career out of politics... it's only when they come round like bloody saints and say they done it for our sakes. They balls up the world for our sakes! An that bloody Margaret Thatcher, I say...

While Churchill was out fighting the war, out on the Second Front with the troops, the other one, bloody ferret-faced Attlee, was back home here making plans what he was going to do after the war. Seeking out ways to line the Labour Party's pockets with Russian gold. It's a wonder old Winston never tumbled him. But then, Jesus never tumbled Judas until it was too late. You know what I mean, the sudden affluence of yer Labour Party after the war. I mean, it was obvious. They was all bloody working class, the lot of em. An if it hadn't been for Attlee, all they'd have had when the war ended was their demob money and their cloth caps. It's obvious – when Winnie's out in Yalta talking to Stalin in front of everybody, bloody Attlee's round the back flogging East Germany an India to Molotov.

Prosperity during the thirteen years of Tory rule when we never had it so good. The last of yer great leaders before yer Tories succumbed to the disease of liberalism and women's lib. Fancy putting a woman in charge! I mean, say she has a baby – they still live together, you never know, he might... one night when he ain't got brewer's droop. How's Thatcher going to feed it during Prime Minister's Question Time? Cos they all want to feed em in public – Esther Rantzen, Harriet Harman. She might be Prime Minister but I bet Denis gives her what for when he gets home. Come on, where's my dinner, he says. Never mind about South Africa, there's a button off this shirt. I wonder what he must think. As he's going out to work in the mornings, all these men come in. I wonder what the copper on the door must think... any other house he saw that, he'd close it down.

Of course, *you* wouldn't like a woman Prime Minister, says Rita. I'm not starting on her because she's a woman, I said. But she's better than any man, says Rita.

Oh, I wouldn't say that, dear! says Marigold. Oh shurrup! I says. I'm starting on her because she's the leader of a government of spivs. She shuffles em about like a bloody card sharp. Flogging off everything decent she is, anything that makes money she sells to her friends. Like Petticoat Lane up in that Parliament some days. They're getting back what it cost em to get her in all right – don't you worry. They're all bloody spivs! There's not one Eton boy in her cabinet. Cos they won't serve under her will they? An you can't expect it. A decent Eton boy ain't gonna serve under a grocer's daughter, is he? A jumped up nobody from Grantham! A woman whose father delivered groceries to their back door. They can see through her. They know her sort. Probably lived among spivs all her life. Brought up in the black market just after the war, wasn't she? With a father who was a corner shopkeeper, an we all know what corner shopkeepers are like – I've never met an honest one yet – rob you blind, they will. Look at em during the war. They always had something under the counter for those who didn't mind paying a bit over the odds – nearly all their trade was under the counter. *She* knocks out half of Britain under the counter.

You wasn't above stealing stuff out of the docks yourself, Else says. Dockers' perks, I said. Anything I brought home was in lieu of wages, my dear. Didn't have to steal it. It was dockers' perks, it was expected of you. A blind eye was turned to it . . .

It wasn't honest, Else says. It wasn't stealing, I said. Well, it looked very much like it, Else said. An if you'd been caught you'd have got your collar felt, says Marigold. Look, I says, I might not be perfect, my dear, I might have my faults, very few of us are saints, I said, but I wouldn't have the cheek to set myself up as Prime Minister an Leader of the Tory Party coming from a background like she does. They've ruined the Tory Party they have, driving decent men out of it they are! I mean, how d'you think yer Queen feels having to meet her, having to invite her home to Buckingham Palace an put up with her ways? Bloody grocer's daughter!

Before Margaret Thatcher, always before *her*, yer Tory Prime Minister come from a good family. Someone of yer Queen's own class. Someone from Her Majesty's own circle. Someone she can mix with and feel at ease with. Someone from Eton an Harrow. Someone who's been brought up to be Prime Minister . . . Like she was brought up to be Queen, someone born to rule. Someone with his own money, someone with his own fortune, someone with so much money he don't need to fiddle, someone who don't need to rob the rest of us, someone who can afford to be honest. Someone who was born to money an knows a bit about spending it. Someone like Harold Macmillan . . .

Super MAC! shouts Rita. Yer, Super Mac! Super Mac, if you like, I said. He's come out of retirement, an he? To try to put her right. He was in the House of Lords trying to tell Thatcher. He told her – if you ain't got the ready money, he said, borrow it!

Join a loan club, Rita says. Yers, in a manner of speaking, I said. It's simple economics. If you ain't got it, do what the Americans do – borrow it. Look, I said, in 1939 when we wanted to have that war with Hitler, Churchill didn't say, We can't have this war with Hitler until we've saved up for it. What Churchill done, he put it on the slate like they used to in her father's shop! We had that war with Hitler on the never-never, cos nobody can afford cash wars. Not unless you have cheap six-day wars like yer Jews do. Well, they could do it, they was only fighting Arabs. I tell yer, by the time they got their discount for cash out of that war, an sold the TV rights world-wide, I bet they showed a handsome profit.

Course, they're shrewd, they're clever businessmen, them Jews. Once they's seen how much yer Muhammad Ali got out of selling his fights to yer telly, an how much yer FA make out of live telly football, it stands to reason – if you got a war, six days of live blood and thunder action, with a result at the end of it – course you're gonna make sure you own the TV rights. Who d'you think owns the TV rights to yer Falklands war, eh? Us! Us! I hope. An why do you think yer Americans saw it before us, eh? Because they paid more for the first showing, that's why.

See, that's what we want in this country – a few Jews in the government. An I'm not talking about shmucks! I'm talking about clever Jews. Not that cartoon Leon Brittan – he looks like Morrie the Fishmonger. Clever Jews I'm talking about. Jews like Lord Grade, yer Weinstein, yer Bernard Delafonte, yer Robert Maxwell, yer Charlie Forte... let them have a go at running the country before it's too late! Better still, let some of yer Pakistanis have a go. Get a few Patels in the government – let them have a go at making a few bob for us. I bet they're running Thatcher's father's shop now better than he did. Or yer Japanese. Better still, let's hire a Japanese government to run things for us, just until we get on our feet.

The End

Epilogue

Bloody politicians! This is their world, not ours! We're just an embarrassment to em, we are. Except when there's a war an they need us to fight it for em! Except when they need our votes an they have to come knocking on our doors like bloody brush salesmen to cadge em off us. They should be made to buy our votes. Pay cash up front for em. In the old days you could get a sack of coal for yer vote. All they offer you now is promises, promises. At least in the old days after the election you still had yer sack of coal. Now after yer election all you're left with is a sack of lies an empty promises.

The only promises yer Member of Parliament keeps is the promises he made to himself. The only better Britain he's interested in is the better Britain he's gonna have for himself. The only new houses he's interested in building is the new house he's gonna build for himself to go with his new car an his new job! Them bits of ballot paper we mark with a cross might only be bits of paper to us, but to him they're gold. Pure gold bloody treasury notes. I've never met a politician, trade union leader, town councillor or any other of the I'm doing this for the betterment of the people bloody brigade, who didn't end up far richer than when he started. Living in this country is like being driven in a car by a drunk who don't

117

know where you wanna go or how to get you there if he did – charging up one-way streets the wrong way, hurtling through red lights. Who you would take the keys away from if you had any sense, or wasn't as drunk as he is...

What we ought to do with all yer politicians when they make a cock-up an ruin people's lives is take em out an shoot em. That way we'd either get good politicians or no politicians at all. Trouble with your politicians, they're all like bloody Wogan – won't let anyone else get a word in. What they should do – might improve this country – is make all yer politicians, all yer make this country a better place to live in mob, make em live in yer slums instead of yer big houses. Put yer Prime Minister's house an all yer bloody cabinet down here, let em live here among some of the people we have to live among, an mix with what we have to mix with. You might see some improvement round here then. Let yer Prime Minister live here for a bit an get mugged a few times, have her handbag stolen, have to put up with some of the hooligans we have to put up with. Let her darling Denis drink in some of the pubs I have to drink in. She might feel more keen about her promises of law an order if she had to live among yer criminal classes like I do. These are yer criminal classes, the ones I have to live among, the ones who can't afford to live in Spain. This is where they live. This is where they come home to. On visiting days at Wormwood Scrubs five charabancs leave this street. No need to go wasting money building prisons, just move the innocent out, an build a wall round the rest of em!

I fought for this country, and what did I get out of fighting for it? Nothing, except a wife who spent her last days in a wheelchair that I had to push everywhere...an got nothing out of that either, except a measly thirty pound which they took off me as soon as she pegged it.

An where I lay me head I have to pay exorbitant rent to a council that's always babbling about what it does for the people. When I fought for this country, what I didn't know, an millions like me didn't know, was, it wasn't my country I was fighting for – it was my landlord's country! We must be ignorant an fools to put up with it. No wonder you only have to put a cross on a ballot paper – the mark of ignorance. An the more ignorant your voters are the better the government likes it. That's why they don't wanna spend money on schools.

I tell you, for all they go on about yer Russia, it's a political system all our governments envy. One party, one vote an no right of choice. It takes away all the uncertainty of elections, dunnit? An for them who don't like it – Siberia!

That bloody Channel Tunnel they're building ... we don't wanna get any nearer to the French, at least I don't. I wanna separate myself further from em! What we should be doing is building a wall, a bloody great wall between us, a bloody great wall that's big enough to block off the whole of Europe! Look at yer French in the First World War. They charged our lads rent for their trenches, an then, when yer Yanks arrived out there, they put our lads' rents up cos yer Yanks had more money. Sod em! I wouldn't build a tunnel to get any closer to them. They say it's to make work. Same as building all them high rise flats made work. They build em badly so they fall down, an then it makes more work. Well, they wanna make work building that Channel Tunnel, let em start it at Belfast, go under England with it – that'll make work. An when it's finished, fill it in again. They wanna make work? That's the way to make work.

What they wanna do is put yer Queen an yer Royal Family in charge of the country like they did in the old days. Course, they've been brought up with a bit of discipline, they have. I mean, all yer monarchs, they're in the Army or yer Navy at no age, doing a bit of service they are, getting their knees browned a bit. I mean, even yer Queen, she was in the ATS. The thing is, when they're born as children, they're born to rule an they're brought up to it. Not like your politicians, I mean, most of them are dragged up. Especially your Labour lot. Come out of the bloody slums they do most of em. That's why Her Majesty should have a veto an be allowed to overrule yer Parliament any time she wants to. In the old days, when your Kings an Queens run this country, we was a force to be feared. Blimey, when the other Elizabeth, Elizabeth the First, when she was up there on that throne an anyone in the world gave her any old back chat, the fleet was sent out an brought their heads back to her.

Look, if yer Queen don't want to be Prime Minister, if she's got too much on her plate being Queen, let Philip become Prime Minister. Make him Prime Minister – he wouldn't need Downing Street with a copper on the door, he's got Buck House with the Army on his door. An he wouldn't have to waste time like other ministers seeking audiences with the Queen, cos he can speak to her anytime he likes which is his conjugal rights as her husband. I mean, he could leave yer Parliament at night an walk home an sort out all the country's problems with her over a cup of cocoa in bed. Or if Prince Philip don't wanna lower himself having to mix with that mob of lying, cheating, self-seekers in yer Parliament, let young Charlie have a bash at it. Instead of Prince of Wales make it Prince of Parliament for your Heir Apparent. I mean, no one wants to be in Wales, but everyone it seems wants to be in yer Parliament. I could write a book about it, I tell yer, but I wouldn't bother!

THE ELSE GARNETT LETTERS
(To her sister Maud)

Publisher's Note

It was impossible to get Mr Garnett to write about anything except himself. So, much to Mr Garnett's annoyance, his brother-in-law Wally has kindly provided us with some letters that were written by Mrs Else Garnett to her sister Maud in Southend. At the time of going to press Mr Garnett has threatened to sue. He told a representative of this company over the telephone, 'If those letters are published I won't have that book in my house.' He went on to say, 'The letters are all lies, and she didn't write them anyway, and besides, her sister Maud couldn't read.' He also said, 'Tell Wally, if I see him . . .'

At this point his money ran out.

Dear Maud,

Alf's ill in bed again so I'll be able to write a bit longer today if
the pencil don't run out. I can hear him moaning up there.
Serve him right – it's his own fault. It's only the drink he says.
That's all it is. Drink – that's all. Well, I know if I bought some
sausages and cooked em for you, I says, and after eating them
your voice started to get slurred, I told him, and you kept bash-
ing into the furniture, and falling over and was up half the night
being sick and in the morning you was sweating like you are
now, I said, and shaking and trembling – I'd call the doctor. And
when I told him it was the sausages made you like that he'd go
and see the butcher, or someone from the council would, and
if he kept selling sausages that done that to people – they'd
lock him up. But because it's in a bottle, I said, you say it's only
the drink. If you ask me I said, I think it's about time you
stopped drinking when it does that to you. It's the grape, he
says, grape and the grain, that's all. It was in the papers the
other day, I told him. It said that drink addiction is more
dangerous than drug addiction. Addiction! he says, it's not
addiction. Habit, he says, it might be habit but he won't have
it's addiction. Anyway, he can't go a day without. I think he's
alcoholic. His father was a dipsomaniac, but if I tell him that
he says don't talk daft – bloody alcoholics! Bloody alcoholics
don't drink normal, not like I do. Bloody alcoholics, I mean,
blimey, once they start they can't stop. Nor can you, I says.
Look, he said, I ain't drinking now, am I? No, I says. Well, he
says, that's what I mean – if I was alcoholic I'd be straight at it.
If you don't go to work today you'll be straight at it as soon as
they open, I told him.

You know Maud, he knows when it's opening time without
even looking at the clock. It seems like a bell rings in his head
ten minutes before they're open. He has a lay down Sunday
afternoon and at ten to seven he's up getting heself dressed
and on his way to the pub before he's awake even. If you want
to see alcoholic, he says to me, old Mr Fraybourn, he's
alcoholic. Mr Fraybourn? I said, that man doesn't drink. He

never goes near a pub. He daresn't, Alf says, that's why. If he, old Fraybourn, if he goes in that pub, he says, all he's got to have is one drink. One drink, that's all. Just one teeny little Scotch, and that's it. Well I wish that's all you had, I told him. But he don't stop there, Alf said. Nor do you, I said. One drink and that Mr Fraybourn he's off, off on it, Alf says. And then it takes doctors and hospitals and psychiatrists and all sorts to get him off it. Well, I says to him, I'm afraid it'd take more than that to get you off it. But when he's on it he's on it for days, weeks, Alf says. You've been on it for years, I told him, ever since I've known him. He was drunk on our wedding night and he ain't been sober since. I don't know how we had my Rita what with his drinking. He says to me, he says, if Mr Fraybourn drinks he can't do his job. Well he's a bank manager, I said. What's that got to do with it? he asks. If Mr Fraybourn gets drunk at lunchtime, I tell him, he can't go back to his bank singing and shouting and making a spectacle of himself and sleep it off in his vault can he? Not like you, I told him. You can drink all lunchtime and right on into late afternoon, I says, in your docks, with your bonded whiskies, and when you collapse incapable, sleep it off in a warehouse till gone nine o'clock at night, and put in for overtime when you wake up. Once he fell into a drunken stupor on the boat, and they had to put him off at Southend and send him home in a taxi.

But it's no use, Maud, you can't talk to him about drink, he brings up his dad, the Prince of Wales, old Churchill. He was a good man, he says, there was a man, he could drink. He could drink as good as anyone. Drink anyone under the table, Churchill could. That man – used to start his day with a drink he did. Had his first brandy, a large one, at ten o'clock in the morning and he'd go on all day into the night till next morning if he had to. And would you say he was alcoholic? he asks me. Yes, I said. Don't talk daft, he says. Greatest Prime Minister we ever had, he was, that's who he was, our war leader. Well, I says to him Maud, I dunno I says, a bit dangerous I think. Start a war, the biggest war in the history of mankind, and put a drunk in charge of it, a man who if he was drinking like you say he was, he'd be arrested and locked up if they caught him in charge of a car. Look, he says, alcoholic or no alcoholic, drunk or not bloody drunk – he was worth fifty of what we got in the bloody Parliament now...

I'll have to go now Maud. Min sends her regards – you know Min, used to live round the corner now lives next door to us, perhaps you don't – anyway I must go over the off-licence and get his medicine before he gets up.

Love,
Else xxx.

Dear Maud,

I hope this finds you as it leaves me. That Mrs Skinner lives in number 10 stops me the other day, she with her daughter, she wants to show me her new coat. Her daughter bought it for her she says. Her daughter's a whore, on the game up West she is – and she knows I know but it don't stop her boasting about her new coat, no shame some people have got. Well I don't say nothing, you know me I just look at her. She bought me this she says, you know showing her coat off. She bought me this, she says, good girl she is. Might be immoral what she does, I mean, some might not approve, but it's only toffs she goes with, real gentlemen some of em and very respectable all of em – she wouldn't go with em otherwise. Don't blame her, says old Gran who's standing with me, wish I'd done more of that when I was young, wouldn't be struggling now on me pension, she says, give it away I did. There was many a lad couldn't sleep at nights thinking of me. I was daft though, I used to do it for chocolate and then share the chocolate with em. Here, you know that old Mr Jackson, says the daughter, he stopped me in the street today an asked me if I had a special rate for pensioners like they have up the pictures – cheeky perisher!

Bet she goes with blackies, old Gran says – an she hears her. Only rich ones, she says, I'm having an affair with one at the moment, she tells us. Very superior person. He went to Eton. His father ate his mother, they didn't have divorce – they had cannibalism. But Bongoola's all right, she says, he's a vegetarian. Nice chap. His tribe get all their warpaint from Elizabeth Arden. Copper, gold, diamonds, you name it – he's got it in his garden, she says. He's into oil a bit too, she goes on. Some of the diamonds he wears are more powerful than Chelsea's new floodlights. I can't meet her eyes, I mean – she's got no shame at all. I'm moving quite a bit in Arab circles these days, she says. Well, they find it cheaper to shack up with an expensive girl like me than ship the harem over. Arab Sheikh I was with only last week said he brought his harem over last

127

Dear Maud,
    I think I'm having a baby. I don't know how. I don't know when.
       Love,
        Else

KARDORAMA

Dear Else,
  It must be an-
other virgin
birth.
    Love,
      Maud

Mrs. Garnett,
~~Wapping~~
High Street
~~London,~~
E. 1

Dear Maud,

    I thought it was mumps. But the doctor says no it is a baby. But I still can't remember how or when.

            Love,

               Else

KARDORAMA

Dear Else,

    He must have been sober one night. Can't you remember?

           Love,

           Maud

CARELESS TALK COSTS LIVES

Mrs. Garnett,
~~Wapping~~
High Street
~~London,~~
E.1

Dear Maud,

    It's arrived. My prayers have been answered. It's a girl and not a bit like him.

            Love,

              Else

year but it took him hours to get it through customs – it's just not worth the fag for a weekend. You know, I've got Jewish blood in me but I get on very well with rich Arabs, and they don't show anti-semitism to pretty girls. I'm not Jewish, her mother says, nor was your dad. No – but the milkman was, the daughter says, you and your cheap milk, she says, you ended up with another mouth to feed. And then she turns to me and as bold as brass she says, I had a Jewish feller a few weeks ago, and do you know, all the time we were at it he was trying to keep the deal open. I had to wait till his carnal desires overcame his business sense before I could get a firm quote. And then he wanted a ten per cent discount for cash. Well Maud you know me I went in and shut the door. But that's not what I wanted to tell you.

What I wanted to tell you about was something I've been missing. I don't know about you but I find the telly boring and what I'm missing is the old cinemas – you remember the Troxy. Miles long that place was from the screen to the back of the gods where we had to sit and all the actors, made them all look like dwarfs, and the balcony was so high it was good training if you wanted to be a steeplejack Alf always said. It was nice in there though – if you got a clear night. Couldn't see nothing though if a bit of fog got up. You remember it used to get a bit misty in there some nights, come off the river. We used to all be shouting, shut that door, keep that fog out. What I'd like to see Maud is if they brought all them old star turns back, you know, Al Jolson, Rudy Vallee, Marie Lloyd. Alf says they can't bring em back cos they're all dead cept the ones who are still alive and there ain't many of them he says. Anyway they was better than what we got now because they was better films you had then, cheaper too they was than what they are now. Didn't pay often though did we? Used to take a bottle of lemonade in with us, fish and chips, faggot and pudding – you can't even unwrap a toffee now without someone complaining. Used to bunk in didn't we? One of us used to pay, and once she got in she'd open the exit doors and let the rest of us in, ha ha ha. Alf says they used to take screwdrivers in with them too and if they didn't like the film they used to take all the screws out and let all the seats fall down, and throw things, stink bombs and bits of fish and chips and faggot and pudding, and pour lemonade all over their heads from the balcony. Ha ha ha laugh it was but we wasn't hooligans, bit high-spirited that's all. We stopped when they put the lights up, we knew how to behave ourselves. We didn't fight with the police or the attendants – not like yer football hooligans, Alf says, we knew when to stop.

But what I mean is Maud sitting here on your own all night watching telly ain't the same is it? You can walk along the front you can. We got nothing like that here, all we got is streets. Must be one of the best things about living in Southend is having the front to walk along. Do you and Wally go for a paddle much? I would. I'd be in there paddling all day. It would do my feet good I should think – it would do Alf's feet good, at least they'd be clean.

Well I must finish just for tonight – I won't finish, not properly – I won't end it, I mean I'll do some more tomorrow see

PTO

If I don't send them all as I write them, see, it will save money – and also it gives you a longer read. So Goodnight and I'll start tomorrow where I stopped tonight, you see that way you won't get confused you'll know where I've started from again because it will be all joined up – do you follow me? Anyway Goodnight sleep well and I'll be starting again tomorrow to carry on where I left off and to tell you more of our goings on here,

I started to sign it and I ain't finished yet.

~~Love,~~ ~~Else~~

Silly me!

I done it again!

~~Love,~~
~~Else~~ x x x x .

131

Dear Maud,

This is the letter I didn't finish, do you remember – I posted it by mistake – you must have been surprised to see the end that wasn't there, the bit I was going to do tomorrow. I think you would have understood it all right if I had done it – because it would have carried on from where I left off. And you would have seen what my plan was then because it would have been there for you to read. But you must have been surprised not seeing it, especially after expecting it like I promised.

Anyway I won't carry on with where I left off because it wouldn't be the same not having sent the first bit to you by mistake and besides in the meanwhile I've had a letter from you and I think I should answer that first – if you think I shouldn't and you think I should carry on with the bit as I started it and want me to finish it please let me know. In the meanwhile I'm pleased to hear about your new dog and so is Alf. We used to have a dog as you know – or didn't I tell you but I think I must have done because I try not to keep any secrets from you as you know. Anyway this dog we had Alf says was one of the best makes of dog you could get and Alf says he was lucky to find it and that the people who'd had it before us was fools to throw it out because they didn't know its value. It had more bones that dog than most dogs have, bones sticking out of it I mean, because most dogs don't have as many bones as our dog had that's why you don't see them sticking out. Alf knows all about dogs because his father had one once and so I suppose the dog was lucky Alf found him instead of somebody else who wouldn't have known how to treat him as well as Alf does. I'll give you some of his advice now which will help you and Wally learn to know how to treat your dog. You mustn't pamper dogs Alf says because dogs don't like to be pampered. They're not human Alf says and so they don't like to be treated like humans – although the dog we had was almost human Alf says and the dog his father had was cleverer than most humans and had an uncanny sense of smell Alf says. His dad could be four streets away and that dog could smell him coming. Although I must say that don't sound so clever because everyone could smell Alf's dad coming even further than four streets away. His father's dog was a ratting dog, Alf says, best ratter in England. And Alf says he's seen them put fifteen cages side by side, each one with a rat inside it, and they've let em all go at once and that dog's gone and killed the lot. And the last one he's killed wasn't more than a foot from the cage. Some people don't believe this story when Alf tells it but it's true. He says the old Prince of Wales seen him do it once and offered his dad four thousand pounds for that dog. I wouldn't have thought they'd have had any rats in Buckingham Palace would you Maud? Anyway Alf's dad wouldn't sell it. Not that it wasn't going to a good home. I mean that would be a good home for a dog that would, Buckingham Palace, I mean, the old Prince was fond of animals according to Alf. But his dad thought too much of that dog, that's why he wouldn't sell it. Alf's dad told him, he said to Alf he said, I'd sooner sell your mother than sell that dog.

Anyway Maud I wish you luck with your dog and hope he turns out better than our dog did. Alf had to have our dog put down. Well it grew into a much bigger dog than we thought it would and it didn't see eye to eye with Alf about where it should sleep – Alf thought it should sleep downstairs but the dog preferred to sleep on the bed alongside of me. I didn't mind but Alf hated to sleep on the sofa. Perhaps your dog won't grow so large. But if it does perhaps it might like your Wally better than ours liked our Alf.

I'll finish here. I don't think longer letters work.

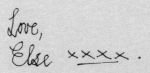

Love,
Else xxxx.

Dear Maud,

I hope this finds you as it leaves me. Min was in here. I don't know why I says that as if it was some news, she's always in here, she's never out of here she ain't – she must find our house more comfortable than her own. It's her Bert. He's worried about the Health Service she says. She says he says it's running out of money and they're closing down hospitals cos they can't get the nurses he says. Of course I never have any use for it myself, I've never been to hospital in my life I tells her. That's what my Bert says, she says, time it's our turn they'll be shut. There'll be no more money left. I wouldn't care to visit one either, I tells her. We've paid though, she says, we've paid in same as all the rest have. Oh yes I says, we've paid in as much as anyone. My Bert works it out, Min says. He sits all night some nights with his paper and his pencil, scribble scribble scribble. He's very good with figures, always has been. Could have been a scholar if he'd wanted to, and what we paid in he says, we paid in enough to go on a world cruise. Well, I says, I'd like that. Must be lovely in the Isle of Wight. Could go there too he says for what we paid in, she says. More than most he says, she tells me. I say to him I do, you ought to go down there and see em and tell em you want some of what you paid in back. We're only poor people she says.

Well Maud, it wasn't an idea I was fond of from the start. I said to Alf at the time when it was first mentioned, when they first brought it up, I told him, I said, I'm not keen. I said, Health Service is all right for them what's going to be sick, I mean if you're a sickly sort of person what always been ill. Well, I mean, you might get some benefit out of it. But if you're not going to be sick, if nothing ever seems to ail you, you're better off saving your money and going off, you know like Maud said on a world cruise or something, to the Isle of Wight – I've always wanted to go there. You've been there haven't you, you and your Wally? I told Min. I said to her my sister's got her own car you see. Her and her husband are proper travellers, labels all over their car they got, you can't see out of the window for labels. That made her jealous because she went on, oh it must be nice to travel, I'd like to go to some of the places you see on television. Though I spose they're not the same if you get there. I went to Margate, she says, but it was nothing like what I thought it would be. It was all nice and sunny on the posters, with golden beaches, but it rained all the time we was there and what with my Bert worrying about the Health Service and that woman who's in charge of it – it didn't do me a bit of good. My Bert says, he says, she says, that Mrs Castle, since she got her hands on the Health Service, she's bought a big house and they've made her husband a Lord and them things don't cost nothing. And that's why when it's our turn to be sick, there'll be no hospitals or nurses to look after us. It's always the same annit? First come first served. If you don't push yourself forward you don't get nothing. Well, I said to her, I wouldn't push. No nor us, she says, but there's some do. They come in and out of them places day and night having things done, operations, all sorts of things they get.

Well she's right there Maud. Her in number 9's had her share out of it. And the rest, says Min. One of the lucky ones she is, since they brought that Health Service in and made everything free she's never been so ill. She got worse as soon as it started. Not fair to us. An it ain't Maud when you think about it. We pay in and if like us you're one of the healthy ones you're one of the losers. But there's some, I won't mention their names – the black ones, they come over here cos they're cunning, they are. As crafty as a wagonload of monkeys they are. Come over here they do and get all the false teeth and false eyeballs they need, wooden legs and everything, and then get two thousand pounds and go home again and start up in business – new men. The National Health Service is fine for them, it's what attracts them over here to get all their bits of surgery done. They go ill in Pakistan or India and it looks like it might cost a bit to treat em, so their bloody government, as Alf says, sends em here – 'Right, England for you, Ali Baba, and don't come back until you're well again.'

135

Some of em even want their tribal marks tattooed on the National Health.

I'm sorry to hear you had to have your dog put down as well. I blame the pet shop, they should tell you how much it's going to want to eat before they let you buy it. I'm sorry to hear it bit Wally but I shouldn't worry about rabies if I was you. If Wally does get em, I mean you are insured and I know it will be a mess if you lost him but Mrs Jackson who lost her husband has got over it now and says she thinks it's better really without him now the funeral's over and all the fuss has died down, anyway if anything does happen and you do have to have a funeral Wednesday is the best day for me – Oh and let me know how much black you'd like me to wear. Don't tell Wally but it's exciting isn't it? It's a long time since we had a funeral in the family.

Well, must finish.

Love,
Else

I must tell you I've opened this letter again. I was going to post it when I saw a lovely black dress in the window at the Co-op and they said if I can wait a few weeks it will be in the sale, the girl told me. So I can wait, what about Wally?

xxx.

Dear Maud,

I hope this finds you as it leaves me. Well Maud this time he's gone and done it. Up in court he was, arrested by a black policeman for arguing with a black bus conductor and then he starts to argue with the magistrate. He's in the witness box, sort of pulpit it is, and he's banging on it shouting at the magistrate – A few years ago they was living up in trees, walking about carrying spears, bloody eating each other they was, now they can drive buses and fly airplanes and become coppers and judges, but not us. We can't become nothing like that we can't. We're not allowed to drive a bike, he shouts. Look, I know my rights he says, don't tell me. Bloody magistrates! They don't frighten me. Frustrated football referees that's all you lot are. You got no law, he says, you don't understand the law. Sit on that bloody bench you do, with your moth-eaten robes on, he tells him. I thought you believed in the majesty of the law, I said to him afterwards. Yes, I do, he says, but not in the magistrates of the law. Look at whatsisname, the builder, the one got thrown off the council five times – he was a magistrate and them flats he built round the corner, they all fell down. And that wasn't all what fell down, he says. Lit flares for Jerry he did, on that town hall he built, hoping they'd knock that down before it fell down. Oh he was very annoyed Maud, well he's never been arrested before. Barbara Castle! he shouts at the magistrate, that's the one you want to blame, she brought that law in, that bloody breathalyser, she brought that in cos she couldn't afford a car and she didn't like to see other people driving around in them. That was the politics of envy that was, he goes on. And look what she's done – ruined the bloody car industry because nobody in their right mind is going to buy a car if they can't drive it when they're drinking are they? Drive it up the pub – that's what you want a car for annit? Go out, have a good time, I mean, blimey, there's some people drive better when they're drunk, he says. Bert's brother does. He won't even get in a car and drive unless he's drunk – he's

137

nervous, terrified he'll have an accident unless he's had a few drinks first. And you can't blame him, he says, the way some of em drive. It's yer politics of envy, just cos yer Barbara Castle can't afford a car, he says. She's got a car the magistrate says, and he should know better than to argue with Alf. All right, Alf says, course most of her voters can't afford a car, that's what I mean. She ain't breathalysing bloody train drivers is she? No. They can drive drunk all over the country can't they, spilling yer soup into yer lap, cos she wants their union votes don't she? Train drivers aren't supposed to drink either, the magistrate says. I know, Alf says, bloody do though, don't they? A drunk in charge of a car, it's a lethal weapon, it can kill people says the magistrate. All right, all right, granted, says Alf, so what about a drunk in charge of the country? He can kill more people, can't he? Breathalyse yer Parliament, my Alf goes on, breathalyse yer Prime Minister. They can go into Parliament and make laws, drunk in charge. Why don't they broadcast Parliament? I heard it on the wireless once, it sounded worse than the pub across the road on Saturday night just before closing. And all this Maud just because the conductor wouldn't let Alf hang on to the back of his bus to save pedalling.

When I think about it I think you done better with your Wally than I done with my Alf. I'm running out of paper now so I better close I seem to use up more paper when it ain't got lines on it but he didn't have any lined paper in the shop where I bought this so better luck next time. I don't think we'll ever be able to get down to Southend to see you and Wally Maud, not unless the brewers go on strike and they close the pubs. Tell Wally bee stings are good for rheumatism. I tried it on Alf but he said he'd rather have the rheumatism.

Love (I've almost run out – I'll just be able to get this on the end of it I think so if I can't write any more you'll know what happened. There you are though. I've done it. Just finished it in time before I get to the end of the paper – that was clever, eh?)

Love,
Else ×××.

I've even got a bit over

Dear Maud,

I hope this finds you as it leaves me. My Alf is upset. He's heard the government is bringing in a law making hateful pigs like him share their property with their wife. Half and half. He says, I can see them getting elected. He goes on, I can see yer rich and yer powerful people voting for laws like that – really annoyed he is – I can see yer rich people like yer Charlie Forte and yer Clore and yer Onassisis and yer Lord Rank and other Ranks, he says. The amount of wives them people have, they'd be broke in a fortnight. The only reason the other two, he says, Liz Taylor and Richard Burton, the only reason they went back together again was because they was both too greedy to have a share-out. Anyway, he says, the time yer bloody Parliament, by the time they get off their bums and pass a few laws or do any bloody thing we'll all be dead and buried. I want to sell this house, I'll sell it, don't you worry about that, he says and I'll tell you about your half, he says to me, your half of it. Your half is stuck to my half and that's where it's staying.

Anyway I don't listen to him. You remember old Gran used to live down the road from us. I went down to see her the other Sunday. She's in one of them places now. Funny farm. Should have been in years ago though she should. Doctors wouldn't certify her though. I mean we all knew she was mad. But not them. No they wouldn't have it. Alf tried hard enough to get her certified, tried to convince them. I didn't want him to, like. But she was a burden, like a millstone around our necks she was. Nothing close she wasn't. Not related or nothing. Just thought she was. Funny down there it is though. That funny farm. Good laugh that is, if you got a Sunday. Like the old joke. A feller walking along down there with a wheelbarrow, he'd got it upside down. Feller says, what you got it like that for? He says, the looney, he says, well, he says if I turn it up the other ways some bloke keeps filling it up. Ha ha ha. Don't laugh, Maud, there's a lot of sense in that. Well they calls em barmy and puts em in them places, but it ain't a bad life. Decent places some of them. Out in the country. Looked after, all your cooking's done for you. Everything paid for if you go National Health. Bit different to us annit? Up at the crack of dawn, work hard all day. Phew, I wish I could get myself in one of them places I tell you that, I'd be a lot happier. They ain't got them bars around them places to stop people getting out, it's to stop people trying to get in. They ain't daft. Anyway Maud I must rush – I hear him coming in.

Love,
Else   x x x x .

Dear Maud,

What you said about the films was right. The only films Alf would ever go to was cowboys. That's when you could get him to go – most of the time before we got married and he started drinking he'd stand on the street corner with a gang of other louts who all thought they looked like film stars of some sort. I don't know who he thought he looked like. That's when he started to wear that homburg thing he wears now. It was after he seen Clark Gable wearing one. 'San Francisco' the film was called. That's when he started growing his moustache too. He wasn't my first choice as you know. They all lived down the poor end of the street. They had no carpet, no lino even – they was bare boards. They had nothing in their house. Six to a bed they slept and ate their meals standing up. His father played the penny whistle and an uncle made noises with his mouth, but culture – that's as far as it went.

No one liked him as a child, his mum said he was hated as a child, terrible child he was apparently – even his own mother wasn't keen on him herself. She didn't want him really, she didn't plan to have him, she always said she could have done well without him. Well she had him late in life you see. She'd given up, thought she was finished and then he came along. Gave her trouble from the start he did. Had a terrible time having him she said and a worse time with him afterwards. Horrible baby she said he was, the worst one. She said the others were little angels compared with him, he used to cry all day and most of the night she said. He wouldn't sleep without a light even when he was a big boy. Had a dummy till he was seven, his mum was ashamed, and he wouldn't go out the back on his own in the dark. His mum had to go out there with him and hold his hand. So I don't know where he gets this culture thing from he's always talking about – he was arguing with Mike and Rita about the coalminers going on strike and Alf said if he had to dig coal he said he hoped he'd do it with a bit more grace than they're doing it and have a bit more loyalty and have a bit more gratitude to the country that gave him a chance to dig coal for it. Which reminds me, for all his talk he's gone out again and not got any coal in for the fire – I'll have to do it now. I bet he's not left the shilling for the light I asked him for either. I'll have to go over the pub after him now – I'm not going to sit burning candles with no fire again.

I'll write again tomorrow Maud if I get time. He's been talking about getting a phone, that'll be nice won't it, if you get one too. We can have nice long talks then – be better than writing and save on stamps too.

Love Else xxx.

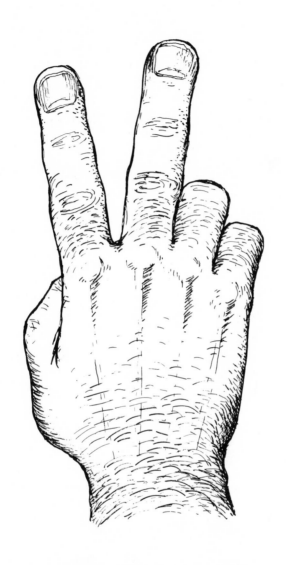

Alf's last word

It's hard luck if you don't like it, but you ain't getting your money back.